THE NORTHER

The Texas Pan American Series

The Norther

(EL NORTE)

By EMILIO CARBALLIDO

Translated with an Introduction by
MARGARET SAYERS PEDEN

Illustrated by José Treviño

UNIVERSITY OF TEXAS PRESS
AUSTIN & LONDON

The Texas Pan American Series is published with the assist-
ance of a revolving publication fund established by the Pan
American Sulphur Company and other friends of Latin
America in Texas.

Type set by Service Typographers, Inc., Indianapolis, Indiana
Printed by The Steck Company, Austin, Texas
Bound by Universal Bookbindery, Inc., San Antonio, Texas

INTRODUCTION

The Norther is the second of Emilio Carballido's
three published novels. The three novels, along with a collection of short stories, comprise the body of published prose
fiction written by this Mexican author whose reputation has
been established primarily in the field of theater. Born in
1925, author of over thirty plays, and the recipient of numerous critical awards, Carballido is widely recognized in
Mexico as one of the country's most important contemporary
literary figures. Only recently, however, has his work begun
to transcend the obvious difficulties of language and exposure and become known outside of Mexico. His short stories
have been translated and anthologized in Germany, Italy,
Russia, and the United States; his plays have been performed in Germany, in numerous Latin American countries,
and in the United States. Now, with this edition of *The
Norther* (*El norte*), Carballido the novelist is introduced to
the English-speaking public.

The Norther, first published in 1958, is the best of Carballido's novels. Like its predecessor, *The Rusty Weathervane*
(*La veleta oxidada*, 1956), it is primarily a novel of character
rather than plot, though technically it is more skillful than
either *Weathervane* or Carballido's third novel, *The Visita-*

tions of the Devil (*Las visitaciones del diablo*, 1965). *Weathervane* has an appealing simplicity of form but is too sketchy to equal the force of *The Norther*, and the longer, more intricately plotted *Visitations* lacks the superb synchronization of style and content that characterizes *The Norther*.

This felicitous accommodation of form to content is responsible for much of the appeal of *The Norther*. The reader soon notes that the narrative moves in two parallel, chronological lines, one of which is the present tense of the novel, the other existing only in the memories of the characters. The past line of action moves closer and closer to the present until it joins with the present; after this fusion closes the circle of time, the characters move forward on a single time-plane only for the duration of the final chapter. This structure imitates the psychological movement of the characters, also basically circular. The two circular lines of psychological movement correspond to the two primary characters, one line within the other. The larger circle is Isabel's line. Encompassing the span of the book, it begins with a seduction and ends with a seduction. The inner circle, relating to Aristeo, begins at the lighthouse, with his first solitary, tentative steps, and ends at the lighthouse, at the moment when he finds that he is completely alone. Max, the third major character of the novel, is merely a tangential figure whose line intersects the circles from time to time. For Isabel, the events in the book constitute a beginning and an end. For Aristeo, they are an introduction, a beginning. Max has neither beginning nor end. He is as near the essence of freedom as a human being can be.

Carballido's sense of place has had an interesting progression in his prose fiction. In *The Rusty Weathervane* setting is important only in a general sense. Because the story requires that the intellectual stimulation identifiable with Mexico City be absent, nothing more specific than provincial atmosphere is necessary; specific descriptions are consciously omitted. On the other hand, place is of tantamount importance in *The Visitations of the Devil*. In terms of English-American tradition *Visitations* is a modern Gothic novel. Its setting is a musty house with hidden passageways and garden walks, which provide a suitably mysterious background for the visitations.

If stylistic progression were logical, then the feeling for place in *The Norther* comes where one would logically expect it—between the extremes of earlier and later novels. The orientation of *The Norther* is firmly established. There are references to the house in which Isabel lives in Mexico City, and also brief descriptions of the boarding house in which Isabel and Aristeo are staying at the seashore. More basic to the concept of the novel, however, are weather and natural surroundings, and many passages throughout the book describe the fog, the beach, the sea, and the atmosphere (not the actual appearance) of the lighthouse. Yet, even these descriptive passages contribute more to the suggestion of an emotional atmosphere than they do to the visualization of physical place.

Carballido consistently suggests more than he demonstrates. It is possible that as an author experienced in the field of theater he unconsciously presents a fictional world in which he expects his public to *see* the action. In this way Max, Isabel, and Aristeo move and develop before an audience which literally observes the background against which their actions take place. The sketchiness of Carballido's prose style, most apparent in *The Rusty Weathervane* but also present in *The Norther*, seems to bear out this possibility. The characters themselves—Isabel, Aristeo, Max—are presented in the same way that place is suggested. The reader *knows* the characters much better than he can *see* them. Isabel's peculiar sexual idiosyncrasies and Aristeo's self-centered reaction to his circumstance are completely familiar to the reader. But there is little, if any, description of their precise physical characteristics. This may once again suggest the dramatic author at work. In creating his story, Carballido creates the psychology and the emotional outlines of his characters, unconsciously expecting that their physical appearance will be readily observed as they enact their roles. The resulting style is certainly pleasing—it avoids the eternal dangers of overdirectiveness—but it may be a style which comes with singular facility to an author with dramatic experience.

The Norther is simple, clear, and direct. There is no ambiguity in language or in events. It is interesting, therefore, and suggestive of fine novelistic talent, that the meaning of the book has been open to widely divergent interpretations. A well-known Mexican critic, in a rather esoteric appraisal, has suggested that the lighthouse functions as a phallic symbol and that Aristeo's final action indicates that he has decided to become a homosexual. This is one interpretation of his novel that Carballido bitterly resents, to the extent that in a second Spanish-language edition of *The Norther*, published in Uruguay in 1967, he altered the text in one section in the hope of precluding any such interpretation in the future. In a letter to me accompanying the altered Uruguayan version, Carballido says: "I think now that NO ONE will think that the lighthouse signifies that Aristeo decided to become a homosexual. Whether he comes back or not is not what is important. Rather that he renew the dialogue that Max had interrupted. And I don't think that Aristeo would reflect a great deal about assuming *any* sexual conduct."

In discussing *The Norther* and *The Rusty Weathervane* a well-known American critic of Mexican literature has stated that Carballido is "utterly pessimistic." Pessimism, perhaps, can be deduced from Aristeo's feeling of being completely alone; his climactic run toward the compellingly hypnotic eye of the lighthouse might be interpreted as a race toward oblivion. It is possible, however, that just the opposite is true, that the multiplicity of sensations that Aristeo is experiencing—the cold, the wetness, the sounds, the taste of salt in his mouth and the stinging of salt in his eyes—may instead indicate an awareness of life. The realization that he is more alone than he has ever been is then simply another concommitant of being alive.

The reader is left free to decide for himself toward what future acts and goals the momentum of *The Norther* propels its characters. For here, as in Carballido's other novels, character is the major concern. More than anything else, it is apparent that Emilio Carballido is interested in what makes and breaks human relationships. The reader will agree that this is one element in *The Norther* that cannot be misinterpreted.

Margaret Sayers Peden

CONTENTS

THE NORTHER

Chapter One

More than the noise of the motor, it was the noise of people that caused Aristeo to turn around. He had been looking at the sea, so quiet, and at the sky, milky silver. Exactly overhead the face of the sun broke out, pale as a convalescent might see it. And nevertheless, there were those people singing, accompanying themselves on guitars, and laughing. A stout woman screamed at every plunge of the little boat; they were a wild and profane group—probably strangers a moment before, they had become intimates in two minutes, the time it took to pull away from the dock and begin to set out to sea.

Aristeo thought about the painting that Isabel had bought for the living room, an ostentatious garden, with women in

wigs and men dripping lace boarding a flower-bedecked boat while many cupids fluttered around them. He remembered it because of the contrast, seeing *La Negra* (he read the name on the side) lurching along filled with girdled fat women and dark men carrying guitars, the motor farting incessantly, happily.

It made him sad. He would have liked to go to the Isla de Sacrificios, too. He would have liked to get to know an island, be part of the group that went sailing by before him, so close they seemed to invite him to jump on board. No longer, though; they were pulling away, headed for the mouth of the harbor with a suggestive up and down rhythm that for an instant wakened obscene associations in Aristeo's mind. He began to think again about islands, about places with palm trees and natives in sarongs. He whistled the song they sang in "Goddess of the Islands." Then he looked at his watch, new, and cheap; it was already time to go back. Isabel would be sitting embroidering in the mosaic-tiled patio of the boarding house, chatting with the straight-haired patrona while she waited for him. He walked slowly, anyway, looking at the big bundles being unloaded from a barge.

"Where do you come from?"

"From Campeche," and the stevedore ran to another place to receive another crate.

Aristeo turned away. It was getting late, he should wait for the streetcar. Never taking his gaze from the sea, he walked to the streetcar stop. He wanted one of the open ones to come, such a novelty to him, with no doors or sides. A closed one came, old and jolting, full of noisy people. The track stretched out behind him while he thought about the sour face Isabel would have. He saw the stop too late (he still didn't know how to tell where he was and he didn't like to ask); he jumped off, and ran, feeling the need to hurry. Before he got to the boarding house he checked his pace, drew a deep breath; he went in.

"Is my aunt here?"

"She's out there waitin' for you." That's how it sounded, and the patrona smiled as the phrase slipped out with musical laziness. (The country singsong regaled your ears with such insistence that after a while, without being aware of it, you were singing, too.)

Here was Isabel, embroidering, sitting in a rocking chair beneath the motionless star of the ceiling fan. She didn't look too unpleasant, nor did she mention the tardiness.

"What did you do all morning?"

Aristeo felt guilty and trapped. *All* morning.

"I went for a walk down by the dock. Are we going to eat now?"

"Right away. Let me get ready," although she was meticulously groomed, her hair piled up, each curl in place, to show off her new tortoise shell comb. She had put on a little make-up; the thin mouth, and the sharp cheekbones, too, bore a trace of color. Calmly, she placed the embroidery on her lap, looked him in the eye.

"You just went for a walk?"

"Yes, that's all. It made me late." (Obviously. Why had he said it?)

"I see that."

The patrona came out.

"Why didn't you take your aunt out walkin'?"

"*I* was the one who didn't want to go out."

"Well, since you were so dressed up, I thought . . ."

Actually, her dress, severe as it was, suggested things outside one's daily routine. More than antiquated, it was without time; it had never been in style, nor would it ever be.

The patrona scolded Aristeo.

"Poor thing. Don't leave her all locked up in here." And, "If you don't come soon dinner will be over, eh? It's very good, beef stew." All this sung in a low voice with mushy consonants and with syllables dropped out.

They watched her go off, twisting up the stairs.

"Shall we go eat?" Aristeo asked.

"Aren't you going to put on your jacket?"

"Yes."

They went to their room. They had taken one room with two beds. When they arrived about a week before, Isabel had registered in *her* name, signing her elaborate signature with a swirling flourish: Isabel Ayala, Widow of Díaz. Aristeo would have liked to sign for himself, but he kept still while the patrona asked:

"With two beds?"

"Naturally!" Isabel smiled, caressing his hair maternally, "He's a big boy now."

He laughed in embarrassment, blushed a little. They gave them room Number 7, on the street, first floor. It was poorly furnished, without quite being sordid. Clean frayed curtains hung at the windows, a washed-out coverlet covered each tin bed. There was a washbowl on a three-legged stand, with two minuscule towels, and bureaus hid the dented misery of the chamber pots.

Now the key had jammed and Isabel took it from him impatiently.

"Give it here."

An hour late. Dissembling, while she struggled with the lock, he turned back his watch. That way he had an excuse if she should renew her reproaches.

"Why didn't you want to see the ocean?" He wanted to underline the fact that he had gone alone because of *her*.

"I've seen it enough already. Is the Norther blowing out?"

"Looks like it," Aristeo lied, since he had heard the opposite. "The sun even came out for a minute." He was afraid Isabel would want to go back to Mexico City, fed up with clouds, and wind, and drizzle.

The door gave way and they went in. He looked at himself in the mirror; carefully he pushed up a pompadour, modeled a deep wave on the side, and admired the effect. He tried a smile that bared all his wide teeth. He would have liked a thick moustache, but he could scarcely raise a shadow, not even touching it up could he make it look like a real moustache.

"Are you through now?" The question was mocking.

He blushed. "Yes, let's go."

"What time do you have?"

He didn't know what to do. Had she seen him turn back his watch? He looked at her face; she had seen, he knew now. This was the face that meant she was setting a trap.

"Why do you want to know?"

"Why do I want to know? I asked you what time it is."

"Let's go to the dining room."

He went toward the door, as if to leave. She stopped him.

"Listen, let go." He shook himself, his heart beating painfully, with the fear and humiliation that Isabel's absurd violence produced in him. He knew what was coming.

"Let go of me, Isabel."

She twisted his hand roughly, almost like a professional wrestler, and doubled his arm up toward his shoulder.

"Is your watch slow?" Mockery, and quiet rage, that's the way she was.

"Look, let me go. One of these days I'm going to let you have it." He wanted to be tough, manly, but his eyes were damp.

"Give it to me then, you big baby. Come on." She doubled his arm harder, but her voice became soft. "Don't ever try to fool me. Do whatever you want, but don't try to make me look silly."

She twisted his arm still more, and he had to lean backward to avoid the pain. So that his head fell on her shoulder.

"I'm not fooling you."

"Good boy. That'd better be for sure. Don't ever try it." Isabel's voice was husky, pitched like a man's, but with maternal overtones.

Then she kissed his mouth, tenderly, with desire, still holding the wrist she was twisting.

"Let me go now, huh?"

She let go. She kissed him again, facing him now, several times.

"Listen, dinner's going to be over."

"Let it be." And she began to unbutton his shirt.

Chapter Two

Aristeo Sanabria had to share, in part, the expenses of his
family. The father, they said, had died. Actually, only the
smallest girl believed this version, and perhaps not even she.
Aristeo remembered at least two different fathers, neither of
whom was his. Aristeo was not the eldest, nor the favorite.
He had a married sister, the oldest, and a younger unmar-
ried one—the blonde. There was a younger brother, Florencio,
and a baby sister, Hada, everyone's favorite. They saw very
little of the married sister; she lived in Ejutla and consented
sometimes to come for the 16th of September holiday. The
blonde, Dora, was a flirt; she went out with all the men from
the market, and one could tell from the daily meal the state of

her love affairs. The best was when she went out with the butcher. She lasted several months with the greengrocer's son, a very handsome boy, and the family practically turned vegetarian. Florencio loved to dress up like a woman, and sometimes he felt like wiggling his bottom more than his sister. But he was very good, his mother's favorite, and he had long tête-à-têtes with her that no one else heard. Once they put him in jail; he got out after three days and told hilarious things about his imprisonment. He didn't explain why they had taken him in, but everyone knew. Aristeo was the only one who berated him; the women defended him.

"Poor thing, it could happen to anyone."

"Not to me," said Aristeo.

"And what about the day you got in a fight? They almost arrested you. And the day you stole the cheese?"

"But they didn't catch me."

And that was the crux of it. Clearly, they can put anyone in jail, with no reason, or for the most trivial cause. There are elements in everyone's nature which are cause enough for being locked up, the family knew it. And the law is uneven. A quarrel with a neighbor, a kiss in the courtyard, a disappearing cheese, everything—urinating, shouting, playing ball —all are jail-germs which may or may not incubate. It's just a bad deal, sickness visited upon the sick. Nothing for it but to be skillful, not get caught.

They lived in Tepito, in the Plaza of Fray Bartolomé. They had one room for all of them. It opened out directly onto an enormous market that stretched for blocks, a place of stolen objects and bloody incidents. They lived badly, but they had never lived any better. Things were more to their liking when Aristeo began to work selling candy in the Mina theater.

Isabel had been married at fourteen. They married her for money, as in the old novels, but she accepted, happy, because her husband was a military man, handsome and mature.

When they were married, he was a colonel. He died a general, General Díaz, and he claimed to be the nephew of the old Díaz, the dictator, whom they had hung in effigy, sumptuously framed, on the main wall of the living room.

On their wedding night, little Isabel was afraid. It was the first wife's bedroom, the gold of the big bed shone in the shadow. Her husband turned on all the lights; he helped her undress, and she wept from shame. Then, he violated her.

He left her sick and resentful. The next day she fled to her parents' house and didn't go back for a whole month. It took her more than a year to experience any pleasure with her husband; she was afraid of him. He wanted to prove his virility; he tried to disguise his mounting years in excesses that first bothered and finally bored Isabel. At times he became furious. "You're as bad as a gringa. Do you want to read the newspaper during it?" Later, he changed his tactics. He brought her pornographic novels, and she was enchanted with them. He brought her collections of prints, which she never tired of looking at. The results, notwithstanding, were depressing. Isabel preferred reading to sleeping with him. Her maximum progress was that she learned to say dirty words and to chat freely with the wives of other military men.

In time she desired him, she greatly identified with him,

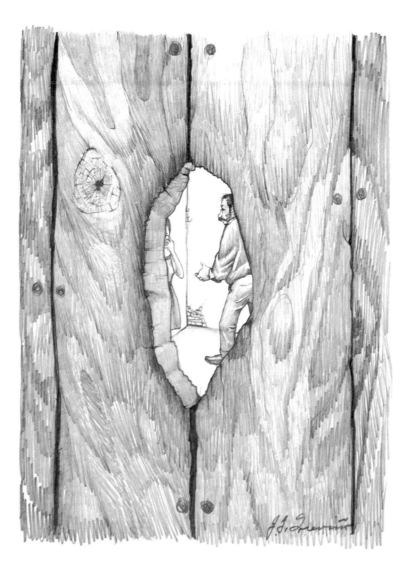

she almost loved him. She pardoned his drinking and resignedly tolerated a venereal infection. He became old very soon. They were married twenty-two years, and the last ten he was more a father than a husband. She practiced the niceties her mother had instilled in her. She read many novels, embroidered many dresser scarves, made all her dresses. When he died she remained in a vacuum which little by little was filled by the movies. She abandoned her army friends, or they abandoned her. In two years she was left almost completely alone, seeing three films a day and embroidering a tablecloth or a coverlet every two weeks. Then she met Aristeo.

Work in the theater wasn't bad. He could see the films, and there were three a day. He didn't earn much, but he found other ways. He could turn in part of the proceeds to the management and keep the rest for himself. He liked the programs in technicolor, especially the ones about pirates. Love stories bored him and he went out to match coins in the second floor lobby, or sat there, thinking things over, or dozing. There, from the corner, he could see curious things, obscene pacts.

That woman now, decent-looking, he remembered. He had seen her alone several times; he had sold her candy and he knew that she wasn't looking for a man. Now he saw her push the door marked "Ladies" and go in. A few minutes passed by and something, without reason, made him think of danger. He walked over to the door and listened. He peered through a crack and saw the scene: there was an evil-looking man, drunk probably, and Isabel watching him from a corner, very frightened but too embarrassed to cry for help. Aristeo entered, and without saying a word struck the man a solid blow in the stomach. The man moaned and left silently. And there they were, still silent, panting, and breathing the air impregnated with urine and disinfectant, hearing only the enormous voices, distorted, distant, of the film.

"Thank you very much."

He said they'd better get out of there. Outside, she lighted a cigarette and gave one to him. She wanted to give him money, something, but she didn't have anything with her. She did find a card.

"Look, this is where I live. I would like . . . (it made her bashful to say "to reward you") for us to have coffee. If you want to come . . . So I could thank you as I should . . ."

She meant to suggest a monetary reward. He thought she meant a sexual reward, and it seemed very tempting, because the old girl still looked good.

Although Aristeo was not a virgin, he had had only two or three experiences. So his heart was thumping when he knocked on the door. "What a big house!" he thought. The only servant, an old woman, returned and let him in after first closing the door on him.

The living room seemed very luxurious to him, with so many *things*, and with the big picture of Porfirio Díaz. The house, a little money in the bank, and her widow's pension was all Isabel's husband had left her. Now that she had them, what had so interested her parents seemed very little.

She took a while to come out. At last she appeared, very

carefully turned out. Aristeo had a picture in his hand. He felt embarrassed.

"Good afternoon. Sit down."

"Good afternoon."

"Over here's better, on the sofa. Were you looking at the picture? It's me, but a long time ago. We'll have our coffee in a minute."

Chapter Three

The newspaper announced a full moon for that night, and, as for the other performances of the evening, gave the exact hour at which it was to begin. Aristeo went to see it come out. Isabel went to the movies.

In the Plaza de Armas a crowd was milling about, men in one direction, women in another. It was disorderly, like a holiday, and all because the band was supposed to play later. The air, cool, tasted salty.

Aristeo walked around twice, looking boldly at the girls; he smiled at one, displaying his big teeth. Suddenly he felt alone, and bored. Someone spoke to him. Hello-o-o. He tried to see her. She was going in the opposite direction, a little girl with small, jutting breasts and string-straight hair. Who was she?

He lost sight of her. She looked familiar, but he didn't expect to run into her again; he went to the sea wall.

There was the sea, alive with cavernous, hypnotic sounds. He walked down the cement strip, lighted and deserted, a long concrete ribbon whose perspective was accentuated by lampposts growing smaller and smaller, while the black expanse lay there, close at hand, boiling. A young mulatto boy swished by smiling at him, and Aristeo thought of his brother, and of his mother. Then he thought about Isabel, but the sea didn't let him think, it was *all*, tenebrous, unpredictable, seething with movement discernible only through little flashes of foam.

Now he could see some small boats tugging on their cables, bobbing up and down. He recognized "La Negra"; someone, a boy, was sleeping on deck.

Then came the loading zone, a long dark dock, covered with canvas and enormous bundles. People were moving in the shadows; hoarse voices, murmurs could be heard. There was light on a double-decked boat, and several men leaning on the rail, looking at him. On another, smaller, there was a lantern constantly nodding assent, and a sweet voice inside was singing a Yucatecan song. Then he saw several launches; he looked at their high masts, their swaying, measured as a metronome.

He hadn't come this far before; he followed an incredible path, narrow as the aisle of a theater; it led away into the sea, where it dissolved in the clamoring shadows. It was both terrifying and tempting. At the end blinked the intermittent flash of a lighthouse. It was so frightening that Aristeo smiled and started down the path.

As he moved away from the concrete walk, he realized that the path was really narrow, slippery, and pitted with puddles. At first he could see nothing, his eyes still filled with light from the sea walk. Now he distinguished two shapes, embracing each other, he even thought he heard a kiss. He went on. Another dark form split in two as he drew near; he heard their excited breathing. He continued. On the ground there were movements, crabs, amphibian creatures that splashed and skittered between his feet; he saw one clearly, and another, coming out of a little pool. Waves leaped on either side. His heart contracted when he saw the great open-palmed slap the wave in front of him made. "It would have dragged me out," he thought, but the fear was savory, and he went forward.

Now he could see better. The path no longer seemed dark, and the beacon, stubborn, passed its light over him again and again. The horizon began to clear. The edges of some large threatening clouds turned from black to rose. "The moon's going to come out," he thought, and hastened his pace. Then he saw the ship, blazing as if it were on fire; it was coming into port and a tiny little tug was leading it by the hand. For some reason his stomach twisted at the sight, and he ran, to get close to it.

He reached the lighthouse. He went up the stairs. Soon he was at the foot of the tower, at the very edge of the platform. He saw the ship advance in the quivering pool of its own light, like a wounded animal floating in its own blood.

Then in the distance the moon appeared, just the edge at first, but as it rose it became a big globe made of burnished luminous matter, emery-polished; red and humid, it burst forth like an escaping balloon lighted from within.

Aristeo tried to see everything, to embrace everything. He smelled the salt, felt the wind; the sea spattered him and grimaced the dark.

"It comes from Portugal."

He jumped. He expected anything except a voice. He turned around and saw someone in the shadow; it was a man. He looked around to see to whom he was speaking, there was no one else. And the other said:

"Want a cigarette?"

"Thanks." He accepted it, restrained.

"Light it by mine, there's a lot of wind."

Smoking now, he lamented the presence of the other, as if it hampered his enjoyment. He decided to pay no attention to him; he turned his shoulder and the other kept silent.

The moon was whole, and continued rising. The ship, a shadow in a halo, was about to dock. He counted the stars—six, seven, eight, there were fourteen in the sky. The clouds were moving fast, windmilling, taking on colors he had never seen. Would it always be like this? Would there always be all this?

He began to be very aware of the other's silence. Perhaps he had gone away. He turned around to see; there he was. He was a young man, thin, or it might be that the seaman's jacket was meant for another body.

"Beautiful, don't you think?"

"Yes." Aristeo wouldn't have dared use the word "beautiful." In his mind he repeated over and over, "What a bitch!"

and even went so far as murmur, "Great!" "Beautiful" it was for sure, but the word bothered him.

"It's breath-taking."

He grunted, "Um-m-m."

That was true, too, but it sounded bad, it had a disagreeable ring. He continued to look. Something had changed. Now he was uncomfortable and he decided to go. He tried to see everything as it had been a moment ago: something was different, now there was nothing but a dark sea and a clouded sky. "What a jerk this guy is," he thought. "He's screwed everything up." Then, why did he make him uneasy? He didn't really understand it, but it was as if a stranger had barged into the middle of a very intimate conversation just when the essential thing was about to be said. "I've got to come back to this lighthouse." But without anybody else.

"Well, see you later," he said.

"I'll go with you," said the other. And he began to walk with him.

Now the path could be seen clearly, very long, only a point where it reached the sea walk. The waves shone reluctantly.

They walked in silence. Aristeo, upset, waited to say no to the other's expected advances.

"Are you studying?"

"No."

"I thought you might be a painter. I write."

"Ah."

"I paint sometimes, but badly. I write well."

"Ah."

"Don't you paint?"

"Me?" What a joker. But he didn't move his head or raise his glance. "No, not me." He felt more communicative. "I'm here on vacation with my . . . (imperceptible hesitation: my lover, or my what?) aunt."

It was the end of the path. They walked on together. They jumped over the ropes, ignoring the other loading equipment.

"I'm just passing through, from New Orleans. We were in Florida, and in Havana. We're going to Mérida next. On a sailing ship."

"On what?"

"A sailing vessel."

Aristeo looked at him with suspicion.

"On a ship with sails? And it's around here, and makes trips?"

"Sure. Haven't you ever been on one?"

"No."

"You want to see the ship? Let's go."

He looked at his watch. It was incredibly late. He was doubtful.

"I can't . . . My aunt . . ." and sharply, "I can't."

Envy shone through his voice.

"Or maybe tomorrow?"

"Tomorrow?"

"Sure. Wouldn't you like to?"

"Well, yes." He looked at him squarely, half smiled.

"At eleven? Because I get up late."

"Yeah, sure. At eleven. But where will I find you? Or how?"

"Well . . . Here. It's on that side. See that light over there?"

He saw a dot that oscillated in the water.

"That's us."

The plural intrigued him, but he didn't ask. They said goodbye.

Aristeo walked lightly, excitedly. He turned around and there he was, watching him, still, near the last lamppost. "Can he still see me?"

The other waved his hand, but Aristeo didn't respond.

Chapter Four

Actually, coffee *was* served. Later, the old servant asked permission to go. It was given, but nevertheless, she hesitated. She lingered in the doorway, looking at Aristeo, and it appeared that she was going to say something. At last she clamped her lips together and went away.

Isabel talked about films, and about the decor of the living room, which he had praised. She was pleased with the serious, preoccupied young boy; she liked him, and she asked herself what he must be thinking. "He must be thinking about how much I'm going to give him." She had already put the bills, twenty-five pesos, in an envelope, ready to slip them to him when he took his leave. She observed him. He was good looking. No, he wasn't. He had the face of a little boy and the mannerisms of a little boy, but when his expression hardened and he frowned, "He looks like a darling little boxer."

He wasn't thinking about money, but about who would initiate the attack. "Her or me?" And she didn't seem to be in any hurry, she talked and talked, and he said yes or no, thinking that perhaps it would be a good idea to clasp her leg. He thought about it so much that suddenly he did it, roughly, and she screamed and sprayed her coffee. He was embarrassed, he pulled out a big clean handkerchief and started to dab at the stain for her. She began to laugh like a wild woman because she had understood what the boy wanted. All at once she saw everything through his eyes, the voluptuous widow seducing the innocent youth. The situation was right out of a novel by Paul de Kock, or someone like that, ridiculous and exciting. Yes, exciting. She was surprised, suddenly, when she noticed the down on the lad's lip. She panicked; he was a man. Then she saw the fright and the indecision and she felt compassionate; he was a child. The child suddenly grabbed her breasts and she screamed again, surprised, and laughed at herself again for screaming. So they ended up in the bedroom, because she refused to have it all happen on the sofa.

They slept a little, and when they opened their eyes the light in the room was livid, and he had snuggled up against her and thrown his leg across her belly. Isabel began to be aware of what she had so enjoyed. And of something worse than that: that she had known intimacy and companionship with that boy. He opened his eyes, with a seriousness that was frightening. He looked at her fixedly, gave her a kiss, and made himself more comfortable against her. "Like a little animal, like a child."

"Little boy, don't go away."

He said no with his head and snuggled up again. Suddenly he sat up in bed.

"I'm hungry," he said.

And she, "What's your name?"

"Aristeo, and yours?"

"Isabel. Didn't you look at the card?"

"Yes, but I didn't remember."

They had supper in bed, she in a wrapper, he nude. They sprinkled everything with crumbs and had to shake out the sheets and put them on again. They spent the night together, and in the morning they made love again.

When he was leaving, about ten, Isabel tried to explain the whole thing to him, and, in a feminine way, throw the blame on him.

"I had invited you over to give you this."

He opened the envelope and his face lighted up. He looked at her, smiling, put the envelope in his pocket and clumsily gave her another kiss. He left.

The old servant watched him leave without being able to believe her own eyes. And when Isabel looked at her from the cynicism of her pleasure, the old woman packed her things and announced that she was leaving. Isabel was very pleased, and the next day she acquired a young girl whose face was pitted with pockmarks.

Chapter Five

Isabel awakened at nine. Her shoulder ached from the weight of the tousled, sleeping head. She heard him breathe. She saw his face—so close—and she examined his features one by one with an attention so intense and so lacking in design that the face next to her became first unknown and then as strange as an object from another world. She saw the nostrils, the shiny skin of the forehead, the stiff eyelashes aligned side by side. She formed the name with her lips, "Aristeo," and it was like a new word from another language. She searched herself, and became aware of the throbbing of her entire body, of the cloth of her nightgown, rolled up to her waist, and the voices and noises of the boarding house became parts of an isolated scene in which there was no one familiar. She shivered, and then she embraced the sleeping boy and kissed

him in the same way that one who is falling grabs for a rope. Then there she was, back again, and the snorting of the boy was part of a secure everyday world in which no one calls for an accounting. The disagreeable sensation in which the terrible black wisdom had welled up had paused. Here were desire and tenderness, right beside her, bearing her away from the mouth of the well in which time was so much longer than her life and the world so much larger and more alien than this room, this house, this town. She sat up in bed. Behind the shutters, the day was still dismal.

She put on a flowered dressing gown and went into the bathroom. The shower had two chains. She pulled one and then the other; still very little water trickled out, and it very cold. Someone beat on the door and immediately tried to come in.

"It's occupied," she cried.

She began to dry herself, chilled and angry.

When she returned to the room Aristeo was already dressed.

"Aren't you going to bathe?"

"It's too cold. I already washed my face." And he looked at her as if fearing an order which would send him to shower.

"Dirty little kid," she thought. At times he bored her; he was so different, so much from another world. She began to get dressed.

She noticed that Aristeo was mulling something over without daring to bring it up. "He must want to go somewhere by himself." She put on her slip, and picked out a dress.

"You know, I met a man."

"Yes."

"A man who has a boat."

"When?"

"Last night."

"A sailor?"

"No, he's the owner. A sailboat." And hurriedly, "He invited me to come on board."

"Ah."

That was it, a plan. But she wasn't inclined to let him go. She said, shrugging her shoulders:

"That's a funny thing, to go see a boat."

So he knew his cause was lost. With a sour gesture he opened the door and ordered:

"Come on, quit painting yourself. Let's go to breakfast."

Isabel, docilely, turned away from the mirror. They left the room. A dark-haired, shapely girl with a broom went by.

"Good morning."

Aristeo realized who it was that he had recognized in the park, the daughter of the patrona.

Meanwhile Isabel was thinking out loud, planning how they would spend the morning.

"I want us to go look for some coral earrings. They have precious things in these curio shops. Some pretty earrings, and then . . ."

Chapter Six

The pillows had been stained with hair oil. Isabel thought that the boy shouldn't put so much grease on his hair. While she was straightening the room (because the old woman had already left), she was overcome by a strange shame, triumphant, exalted. Astounded, burrowed into the deepest part of her being, she watched herself singing outdated songs, saw herself changing the sheets, merry, remembering. Many details kept coming back, and often they were the most intimate, the most obscene. And she wanted him again, and was ashamed again, and she smiled.

All at once she realized that the boy wasn't coming back, and that she would never dare search him out. Then she stopped cleaning; she felt old, fatigued, "a dirty, hustling old woman." What had she come to? "Never again," she promised herself, and thinking about the movie for the day, she had a great shock; she would have to look for another theater, because *he* worked there.

Aristeo told the adventure many times. To his friends in Tepito, to the other vendors. He tried to get them to remember her:

"Don't you remember? She comes here all the time."

He described her, detailed intimacies, exaggerated the money received, the number of assaults, and the hidden excellences of Isabel.

"She's really something," he always concluded.

The following week they showed something with Jennifer Jones, and it seemed to Isabel that she had never wanted to see a film so much. She dressed with great care, and although she tried to keep her eyes on the floor as she entered the theater, she couldn't take her eyes off the concession stand and the two vendors who were coming down the stairs. Suddenly it seemed that she couldn't remember what the boy looked like, and that she would never recognize him.

One of his friends ran to tell him.

"Listen, I think the old lady's here."

"Where?"

"On the second floor. Go see if that's who it is."

Aristeo rushed up the stairs. He looked among the empty seats and found her; it was she. He ran up to her, jovial, and squeezed her arm.

"What's new? Why haven't you come?"

She, her mouth dry, smiled.

"I couldn't. How are you?"

"Want a piece of candy? I'll treat you."

She accepted, and since his friends were watching him back there, he sat down next to her and slipped his arm across her shoulders. Later he asked:

"What time are you going to leave?"

She guessed his intention and didn't know what to say. He added:

"If you wait till the end, we'll go together."

She consented. Meekly, she saw the Jennifer Jones picture twice, plus one about pirates and one about cowboys. The coyboy one was showing again, and she didn't understand what was happening—all the crowds and the shooting. More than halfway through, he arrived:

"Let's go now," he said.

They went out arm in arm, Aristeo bidding goodbye to all his friends in a loud voice, and Isabel red with embarrassment.

The next two times he went to the house. The third time she went to the theater and provoked an uproar among the vendors, but when one of them whistled, Aristeo punched him in the mouth.

After two months they were seeing each other regularly, every week. She began to look at him with critical eyes. She bathed him, she made him cut his hair a little, and she refused to let him use so much hair oil. She bought him shoes, underwear, then shirts and pants, because he said he would like them. He seemed intelligent, and she wanted to make him study, to make him "somebody"; she listened to him tell about his house and his neighborhood and thought it wouldn't be a bad idea to bring him to live with her. But that frightened her, it seemed like an obligation and a problem, and it had been a long time since she had exercised her will. As it was, everything was pleasant, and although she had to force herself to be cynical when she looked at the situation head on, she always found some excuse to look at it from the side, in order not to put a name to things. She made for herself the illusion that it was just a brief game, practically nothing. "Or don't I have the right?" she asked herself; but she never answered.

After three months she surprised him squeezing the belly and the breasts of the servant girl, pockmarks and all. With no further ado she jerked him out of the kitchen, slapped his face, and then threw him on the bed. For a moment she imitated the tones and gestures of her dead husband; she threw herself on the boy, shook him with mannish strength, then kissed him fiercely, and ended by taking off his clothes. Later, she really enjoyed thinking about the scene, as if it had been staged, a game, or a joke. So, like a secret game that she alone understood, she repeated several times the violence which led to the bed. She didn't analyze why, but she enjoyed a curious, histrionic delight in being the active, the aggressive, one.

Aristeo was humiliated at the first blow. He decided to return it, but he couldn't. Isabel was no stronger, but he respected her and feared her a little, like his own mother when she fell to scolding him. The finale was what made him the angriest, when he saw his clothing flying through the room and the woman, scarcely heeding him, carrying on as if she were violating him. He stopped seeing her, but she came to look for him at the theater, and he surely wasn't going to let himself be struck in front of his buddies. Furthermore, she was to his taste; older women are always expensive, or sick. But not this one, and in addition she gave him things, money. He never thought of their relationship in terms of affection; Isabel was a fact as real as his family, and Aristeo soon became accustomed to accepting her with the same passive complacency which bound him to his mother, or to his brothers and sisters.

Chapter Seven

The sea was still choppy and dirty-looking. A palely sunny streak showed through like an intermittent signal light; it rolled for a few moments in its own reflection, but after two or three tumbles it was erased by a gust of gray wind that left behind no trace of warmth or light.

Isabel, with a shawl over her shoulders, was embroidering great cross-stitch roses; she repeated, "You're crazy, you're going to freeze," each time that Aristeo, shivering, came close to her.

Because it was deserted, the beach seemed enormous. There was no one in the lifeguard's chair, tall as a giant's. Farther back were the dressing rooms, some open, some closed; they were empty and from time to time the doors slammed dryly. Some distance away a couple of fellows who

looked like fishermen were pulling old clothes back on over their still-wet bodies. And that was all. Two pelicans floated confidently near the shore. A few gulls, farther out in the sea.

Aristeo ran, to get warm, and Isabel watched him grow small on the abandoned beach. She, in her canvas beach chair, continued embroidering. She liked that sea, but it made her sad. She felt like whispering something autumnal and faded, like some verses she was trying to recall: "await the falling leaves," or perhaps "youth, divine treasure." But that wasn't really appropriate. It wasn't autumn, it was the norther, and even more than the wind, it seemed to be a state of mind. "Nostalgia," "distance," "horizon," were words which came and went with no apparent connection, suggested by the leaden sea and muffled sky.

Aristeo arrived at a run, the hair on his body standing on end, excited by the exercise.

"Where's the booze?"

She looked through her sewing basket and pulled out a flask. He took a swallow and invited her with a gesture. She, reluctantly, drank too. The warmth of the liquid felt pleasant.

"Aren't you going to get dressed yet?"

"No." And he huddled up next to her legs, like a wet puppy seeking warmth. Then, without warning, he sprang into movement again. Isabel watched him run toward the water.

"Don't go out very far!" she called, because he didn't know how to swim.

He didn't hear her. He was already jumping and kicking. The waves tumbled him over. He coughed and gagged. It was like watching him wrestle an enormous domestic animal.

The stranger stopped a few steps away. He looked at her, and smiled with her. Then he turned his eyes toward the puppet that the waves were tossing about. Isabel thought, "That's the way they all are here, forward, and pushy." This one was slim, with large pale eyes, clothed in a seaman's jacket which undoubtedly did not belong to him. For a moment she thought him handsome. She waited for the intrusive greeting with which the port-dwellers invade the lives of strangers, but he remained silent. He wore tight dirty pants; she was rapidly becoming convinced that he was an undesirable character, and wished he would go away. Even so, she looked him directly in the face, only to be immediately embarrassed. "He's going to think I'm flirting." She began to embroider with redoubled meticulousness, still aware of the insistent proximity of the other's presence.

Aristeo came running. He slowed down when he saw the man, who was smiling at him, broadly. "Who's this?" Aristeo motioned with his head.

"Ah." He gave a long "ah" of recognition.

"Yes. Why didn't you come?"

"To the boat? I couldn't."

He felt uneasy. He didn't know what to do. Isabel raised her head. The stranger looked at her now.

"Is this your aunt?"

"Yes."

"Who is your friend, Aristeo?"

Her question pointedly ignored the nearness of the other.

"He's the one from the boat."

He was always smiling. He held out his hand without speaking, and she had to take it, expecting the customary words of courtesy. He didn't say them, and finally she muttered:

"Pleased to meet you."

"And the boat?" Aristeo asked, dancing about, hair standing on end with cold.

"It left. I stayed here."

Aristeo began to dry himself. Isabel looked suspiciously at this individual who was no longer a boy, although at times he seemed so. He must be about . . . twenty three? Or a little more. He made her feel assaulted without being able to analyze why.

"Give me another drink," Aristeo asked.

She held out the bottle, watched him drink.

"Want some?"

"O.K." the other accepted. He took a small swallow.

Isabel wiped the mouth of the flask, and closed it.

"I'm going to get dressed."

So, running, he left them alone. Isabel was really annoyed when the man sat down in the sand next to her. "Now he's going to talk about the Norther," she thought. He said:

"My name's Max." He took the embroidery from her. "How pretty. Do you paint?" He didn't wait for an answer. "This is embroidery by a person with an artistic sense. Very good design."

"It's . . . it's a pattern from a magazine," she murmured, taken by surprise.

"Yes. They're all alike. But the working of the thread . . . Very good color, it gives dimension. Very pretty." He handed back the cloth. "How old were you when you began to embroider?"

When Aristeo arrived, dressed and happy, he saw nothing strange in the fact that they were chatting about Isabel's mother. They continued for several sentences before they noticed him. Max got up and punched the boy, twice. Aristeo put up his guard. They boxed a few seconds. Max lowered his arms.

"Where are we going to eat?" he asked. "Everyone pays for his own."

Isabel wanted to say something. She picked up her things. That's the way the port people were.

"Are you from around here, Mr. . . .?"

"Call me Max. No, I'm not from here."

Chapter Eight

For a while, she didn't know what to do about the maid. "The fool is going to think I'm jealous." She wasn't, but the girl's embarrassment was contagious, and she could no longer look her in the face. She fired her.

When she watched her leave, pretending to cry, with her bundle of belongings, she felt very pleased and lettered a sign to put in the window: *Servant wanted.*

A short fat girl arrived, with shifty eyes. She seemed too young. The old woman she had had before came back, humiliated, to ask for another chance.

"I didn't fire you," Isabel said, but let her go, because she wanted neither judges nor witnesses.

A woman from the coast region came too, tiny and emaciated. She worked for the people next door, but she had had

enough of them because they had several small children.
Isabel looked at her gray hair and flaccid body. She accepted
her. Besides, she already knew her.

She turned out to be jovial and talkative. At the least
provocation she would tell the story of her life, or talk about
Veracruz. After the first night that Aristeo spent in the house,
Isabel watched the woman out of the corner of her eye, waiting for some gesture or some tone in speaking: nothing. And
she wasn't lazy. She decided, with relief, that she was a
very good servant.

In Aristeo's home they found out right away that he had a
lover. He had already spread the news. His blonde sister was
the first to find out, through her sweetheart. His mother joked
with him about it; with complete naturalness she talked about
it and wanted to know where "his woman" lived. Aristeo, annoyed, told her the general area. Florencio was the first to ask
for things: he had seen some divine pants. Why didn't Aristeo
get them out of his old woman for him? The mother was the
last: she thought out loud that Aristeo's "friend" could well
afford to help them pay the monthly rent. He said nothing,
but was furious because they always took what was his from
him. Nevertheless, he did get Florencio's pants and the rent
that the mother wanted.

Her occasional insomnia was wont to come without apparent cause, perhaps from one cup of coffee too many.
Aristeo stayed the night more frequently now, although not
every night. He was beginning to tire her a little. He was
too young, with a direct, healthy sensuality, uncritical. Isa-

bel's old indifference for repeating the same acts seemed about to return; she was more conscious of it at the times she couldn't close her eyes, when she lay looking at the dark ceiling. She heard her lover's breathing, and felt that *she* was included by force in the familiar panorama of night sounds: the creaking of the furniture, the water dripping in the basin, the noise of the streetcar. Then she compared this sleepless Isabel with the other, almost irreconcilable at the moment, the one who used to give medicine to the dying General, or with the earlier, even more distant one, crying because she missed her house and her parents. What relation was there among them? What was this chain of different Isabels that ended with the present and seemed to suggest none in the future? Suddenly, closely associated with the breath of the one next to her, there arose a sharp, barely rational fear: he was taking something precious away from her. What was he giving *her*, besides this ennui, this excessive, if comfortable, warmth, this mutual abandon in which they were living like two sleeping bodies? What was there in the whole thing that was not a little (a little!) ridiculous?

She turned on the radio on the bureau. The early morning sounds of the city filtered gently into the room. There were programs from cabarets; the announcers sounded a little inebriated, and one could hear reluctant applause and sounds from the audience. Several women sang nasally, orchestras played noisely. This all came very quietly, a secret, mysterious tumult, between commercials and bursts of static. Isabel had never been in a cabaret. And Aristeo? She had never asked him, because she knew he liked to exaggerate, even invent, experiences. She turned off the radio as sleep was slowly coming. And with sleep came the sensation of having lost something, of having never achieved anything.

After one of those nights, waking was painful. She saw everything through critical eyes. He made noise when he was eating, he said crude things, he was vulgar. What did the two of them have in common? Her family had been ordinary, her dead husband vulgar, but the vulgarity of Aristeo was different, young and aggressive—it had to be corrected, or accepted, and the two things seemed impossible.

She watched him eat breakfast, she observed him as she would a stranger and felt no desire to speak to him. The servant and he chatted, but their voices were more sound than meaning. Aristeo seemed to become aware that something was wrong:

"What's the matter with you?"

"Nothing." And she patted his hand, to dissimulate.

Isabel longed to be alone. The moment arrived; the house became hers again; there was time to embroider, or to read the engrossing stories she bought on the magazine stands.

Sometimes, though, she missed him, and could hardly sit still until she heard the sound of the knocker. Then she ran to open the door herself, and it was she who dragged him to bed. Undressing him, she reflected an instant. She would have preferred that they do other things, not knowing exactly what.

The servant went to her hometown for four days. Her father was sick, she said. She came back telling marvelous things about the port city; it was so pretty, so big.

"And where are you from," Isabel asked Aristeo.

"From here."

"And your family?"

"From around Toluca."

"And you've never been in Veracruz?" the servant asked.

"No. I sure would like to go."

"I went once, with my husband . . ."

And she remembered a very clean boarding house, with rattan furniture and shell curtains. She also remembered a dance, some entryways, and some friends she had never seen again.

"It's been so many years now. I imagine that things must have changed a lot . . ."

Chapter Nine

They had coffee outside at "La Parroquia." There were more people inside than out and the ceiling fans were still. They watched Max coming, and he saw them while still a long way away. He made that gesture of his, raising one hand very high. He didn't want to sit down.

"Coffee with milk! What are you doing here? Come on, I'm going to treat you to something."

He made them finish up in three gulps and took them to the other side of the plaza, to the entry area of a noisy cantina, filled with foreign sailors.

"A Dutch ship came in," he explained.

"And your sailing ship?" Aristeo asked. "Aren't you going to go on traveling?"

"I had . . . a misunderstanding." He called to the waiter in English, "Three mint juleps."

"Three *menyules!*" the latter said as he walked away.

"There are two cities in the world in which to order mint juleps: New Orleans and Veracruz."

"And what kind of drink is that?" Isabel asked.

"You'll see."

And they saw. Wide, squat glasses, filled with fresh mint and ice. They repeated the order—on Isabel, because Max made it clear that he couldn't pay for another round.

A ruddy, hairy man embraced one of the sailors as they were coming out of the entrance together. Max seemed to recognize the man because he jumped up and went toward the two. The sailor backed away a few steps. Max and the man argued violently, in English. The man broke off the discussion with a gesture and a tone of voice still more violent. He pulled a billfold from his pocket and gave money to Max. Max said something sharp and contemptuous, which infuriated the man even more. Max returned and sat down again.

"I'll pay for the next ones," he said, tranquil, as if nothing had happened.

"What's the trouble?" Aristeo asked.

"Nothing. He owed me money, and didn't want to pay."

"Is he a gringo?"

"Yes. He's the owner of the sailing ship."

They watched him leave, with his Dutchman by his side.

It was the third time they had been with Max. The first was on the beach, when they had gone on to eat together.

Max had taken them to a filthy little inn with long benches, where, he said, the food was excellent. They gave them a soup swimming with fish scales that stuck to the roof of the mouth; then octopus, which really was good. Max talked incessantly—about Havana, about New Orleans jazz, and the oh so poetic canals of Florida. As they left he asked where they were living. Then they said good night. Isabel, watching him stroll away so casually, was bothered by a vague impression of disorder.

"How did you meet him?"

"At the lighthouse. He's a good guy. I like him."

Not so, Isabel; because he "came on strong," and acted like a close friend. Because he never asked questions, but observed so much. And for another reason.

They walked toward the boarding house, out of inertia, since they weren't going to eat there. The stranger had been a powder flash which left them now in the half light of vaguely uncomfortable sensations.

"Let's go get some ice cream," Aristeo proposed.

"All right."

They knew now to go to the park, and to the ice cream stand. Eating the ice cream, slowly, Isabel thought that their trip was purposeless. She hadn't really enjoyed herself and was beginning to miss her own house. The disproportionate feeling of happiness she had experienced on arriving had not been repeated. The town was becoming a series of senseless outings. The things she had bought seemed unsuitable. She touched her earrings. She continued eating cold, sweet spoonfuls. She was completely alone. Aristeo—who knew where he was? Then, immediately, she knew.

"Hey. What a swinging town Havana must be!"

"Yes." The theater was just opposite them. "Look, there's a María Félix picture. Shall we go?" She hoped he wouldn't accept.

"O.K. Let's go."

The following night, the patrona, very excited, knocked at their door.

"A man's here looking for you."

Of course. Max, come to take them to the breakwater.

"With this wind?" Isabel refused.

He stayed to eat dinner with them, payed for his part. He seemed bored, restless.

"Let's us go," he proposed to Aristeo.

"O.K."

"I'm not going to stay by myself," stated Isabel.

That made Aristeo angry, he was getting ready to say something, but Max already had another plan.

"Do you know how to play poker?"

Both of them knew. Since other guests were coming to eat, they went to the patio. The patrona had cards and lent them to them. Max shuffled first.

"I'll deal."

Aristeo immediately became animated. While they were playing, he began to ask questions.

"Listen, how are the gringas?"

"I'll pay to see. Gringas?" Max shrugged his shoulders. "What do you mean, how are they?"

"Well . . . three of a kind."

"I have nothing, an ace."—Isabel.

"You have a straight, you win, Isabel," Max said.

"Oh." She did, but his sudden familiarity startled her. She gathered in the pot, looked at him with surprise, but he seemed unaware of any change in his behavior.

"You deal now, Isabel."

He repeated the familiarity. She shuffled clumsily.

"It's ages since I've played. Cut." She dealt.

The daughter of the patrona came to watch over Aristeo's shoulder.

"Say. With a wind like this, how do you sail in a boat like that?"

"You don't. You stay in port."

"But didn't the boat go out?"

"I want two," Max requested. Isabel gave him the cards.

"Don't lean on me," Aristeo said to the patrona's daughter.

"Oh, go on."

"Well, bring a chair. You're digging your elbow in me."

The small girl moved back a few steps, was about to get a chair.

She met Isabel's eyes, and decided to go.

Aristeo was dealing now.

"Listen."

"What?"

"Where do you live?"

"Near the Customs House."

"Where is the Customs House?"

"We'll go later."

"Are you going to stay here to live?"

"No, I don't think so."

"Are you going to Mexico City?"

The other hesitated a few seconds.

"No. I don't know. I want to travel."

"Where?"

"Anywhere. There's a lot to learn."

They continued playing. Isabel wanted to ask him what he lived on, but she hesitated about how to address him. Finally:

"Max, what do you do?"

"I write."

So that's what he was, a writer.

"And what . . . what have you written?"

"I'm doing a novel."

Nevertheless, Isabel knew that writers died of hunger. "He must be dying of hunger."

The patrona turned out all the lights except one, and circled around as if she were waiting for the game to end. They finished it.

"Wouldn't you all like to go out for a walk?" Max proposed as he was leaving.

"No. Heavens, no." With a trace of "what madness!"

"And you?" Casually, not looking at Aristeo.

"Well . . . no." It made him feel weak. If only Max would take him to the red-light district. But he didn't have any money. "Tomorrow."

The next day they didn't see Max. It wasn't until the day after that they ran into him in "La Parroquia."

Chapter Ten

With her wardrobe open and her suitcase on the bed, Isabel selected what she was going to take. Aristeo had already gathered his things. The radio was on; he was doing steps of the cha-cha-chá across the room, with precise gestures and serious conviction. Suddenly he grabbed her by the waist and she laughed, with embarrassment.

"Let go, I'm ticklish."

"Since when?"

She continued packing. He dug into the closet and pulled out a big album, its binding a little loose. He leafed through it.

"And these, are they you?"

"My parents. Put that down, it's real old."

He paid no attention. He turned some more pages: stiff faces, yellowish pasteboard, moth-eaten.

"And these?"

"My grandparents."

He made an appreciative gesture. Then came the aunts and uncles, and the parents again—all dead. The album evoked memories of a long series of wakes. Then came two disagreeable cousins; she visited them every month, and they returned the visit once in a while. They didn't like each other. The two women counted on benefitting from her death, but Isabel thought they would die before she did. "And I wouldn't leave them anything, anyway."

There was a ninety-two–year–old aunt to whom she took little gifts from time to time, but she was pretty far gone and never remembered exactly who Isabel was.

"This is you, right?"

"Yes, fifteen years ago."

He took the photo from the book, put it in his pocket.

"Give me that. What do you want it for?" although as his action saddened her, it also flattered her. "Sure, since I'm young there."

"You're better now, I swear." He squeezed her bottom and continued dancing across the room.

She thought several things:

"Could it be he loves me?"

"He's doing it to flatter me."

"I hope he *doesn't* love me."

"Why should I hope he doesn't love me?"

"This dress is real cool, and this blouse . . ."

She had a vague feeling of not wanting to owe him any-

thing, neither the pleasure nor the companionship. It was
better to give him things—money.

"You need a new suit, for the trip. And some white pants.
We'll go buy them this afternoon."

"Good deal!" Happy, still dancing.

They went by train, in the daytime, because the night trip
would have posed the problem of buying one, or two, beds,
and either solution filled Isabel with confusion.

The maid showed as much enthusiasm as if she were going
with them.

"Don't let anyone in. I'm going to write you where we'll be,
in case anything comes up."

"How many days will you be there?"

"A week, or ten days."

"Two weeks, two weeks, there's nothing we have to do,"
from Aristeo.

"They'll let you go at the theater."

"No."

But the real excitement began when they got into the taxi.
It increased in the station with the loud ringing of the bells
which announced their departure while they ran down the
platform. He carried the suitcase on his shoulder and was
more nervous than she.

"Hurry, hurry, it's starting!"

They fell into their seats as if they had stormed a fortress,
although there was more than enough room in the coach.

And when they started, Aristeo opened the window and
stuck his head way out so he could watch the city fall away
behind them.

Chapter Eleven

The drinks had made them happy. They walked to the jetty. The wind had died down and suddenly a salty, humid warmth spread over everything, as when a flask breaks.

It was Thursday, again. The plaza was crowded with people, and as they walked away they could hear the beginning sounds of a brassy waltz. They sat down on a bench facing the sea, watching the boats swaying like cradles, or rocking chairs. Couples walked by; groups of girls in low-cut dresses went by giggling and pressing close to one another. Silently, they looked at the water and at the people.

Isabel felt sleepy. It was the alcohol. She was very satisfied, she lacked nothing. She rose:

"I'm going to sleep. Don't get up. I'll go by myself."

"Good. I'll be there in a minute."

"Good night, Max." They shook hands.

"See you tomorrow."

They watched her as she slowly walked away, unconcerned, almost young.

"Let's go for a walk," Max proposed.

They did, in the opposite direction.

"Listen, do you know where the district is?"

"Yes."

"Shall we give it a whirl? I've got the dough."

Max shrugged his shoulders and walked on, paying no attention.

They stopped in front of a big fountain, silent, looking at the stone fishermen. Aristeo wondered whether Max didn't have any money, or what? He looked at him. "What the hell's the matter with this guy?"

Like peninsulas, the last benches advanced in the direction of the sea. There they sat down. Behind them was the large glass box of a solitary, lighted building; the soft glow that fell on them intensified the silence. The sea did that; it hypnotized, created a hollow silence with dark little licks of its tongue; it erased immediate time, it created a greater time charged with unknown transcendencies. Max began to whistle something sweet, a long melody, which stirred Aristeo strangely; suddenly he stopped:

"Let's go together," he said.

"What?"

Aristeo's voice was choked. He coughed; he hadn't understood the proposal, but the words had frightened him for some reason.

"What did you say?"

"Let's go off together. Wouldn't you like to travel? I'll get a boat."

Now Aristeo's heart really was pounding. He was about to answer. He looked at the other very closely. He shifted his eyes. The wind rose again, pushing clouds, blowing away the heat.

"Don't tell *me* you have a boat."

"We can work our way. I spoke today to a man whose ship is going to Havana."

"Listen. Isabel . . ."

"Yes?"

"Well . . . she's my woman. She isn't my aunt."

"Sure. That's what I thought. She would give you money, wouldn't she?"

"Well, not to go away."

"Naturally. You wouldn't tell her you were going away. I have a little."

They looked at each other. Aristeo started to ask a question: "Why . . .?" He interrupted himself. He looked away. "It's just that she's been a good old girl, I swear. And . . . she's always been a good old girl."

"Who else does she go with? Isn't she married?"

"No. She doesn't have anyone. Just me." It filled him with pride to say it, for the first time, and it added a new value to Isabel. "She's a widow."

"A widow? And she has no one but you?"

Max was looking at him with raised eyebrows, a smile hovering on his lips. Aristeo didn't want to seem too naive, nor did he want to recant.

"Ah, what the shit? What difference does it make to you?"

Max got up. He seemed angry, perhaps offended would be more accurate. Aristeo wanted to add something, but the other turned his back. "Well, all the same. . . . Havana?" It was a name that echoed with bongos, rhumbas. It was an island. Or was it?

"Hey, is Havana an island?"

"*Cuba* is an island." Max grasped his neck softly, as one takes hold of the neck of a puppy. "So? Are you getting brave?"

"Well . . . well, we'll see."

"Yes?" Shaking him a little, affectionately.

"No. I don't know. Let's go." Getting up, because his friend's fingers felt so odd.

"And how about that old woman of yours?"

"What about her?"

"Are you going to tell her? If you tell her, she won't let you go."

"Well, I told you I'd see, didn't I? Just what the fuck are you laughing about?"

"Nothing."

And they spoke no more until they arrived at the boarding house door. There, Max clapped him on the shoulder and said softly:

"See you tomorrow."

Chapter Twelve

They were bathed in sweat. Heavy darkness slipped by outside the window; lights from villages were less frequent than that from fireflies, and above the murmur of the wheels one could hear the din of insects.

"Serapes!" came the cry.

"Don't you smell it, Aristeo?"

"What?"

"It already smells like the sea!"

Stopped for a moment, starting again, watching the coconut vendors melt away in the shadows.

"Coconuts!"

Violent, noisy activity told them they had arrived in the

port town. They received cards from four or five boarding houses, and several little boys, jaundiced, thin, straight-haired, fought over them as over a possession.

"The Señora is already coming with me!"

"No, she's coming with me!"

"You're coming with me, aren't you, Señora?"

They were besieged by high, singing voices from the moment the train glided into the station until the last cry:

"Veracruz!"

Aristeo shooed them away with his hand, as one scatters a cloud of mosquitos, when they attempted to take the suitcases out of their hands. They shouted obscenities and ran after other passengers.

The crowd surged about them, people ran, shouted, made an extraordinary racket. They seemed very much like the happy spectators at a fire.

They had to take a taxi. Isabel tried to locate the boarding house, and finally gave the driver the only address she remembered:

"Campana Lane."

When they arrived at its entrance, Isabel asked the driver:

"There used to be a boarding house around here, very clean...?"

The driver pointed to a sign hanging about twenty steps away:

"Must be that one."

"Yes, I think that's it," knowing that it wasn't.

They went in. Black and white mosaic tile, ferns, rocking chairs, the hum of the ceiling fan. It was as if a large, warm

aura of contentment floated in the quiet air of the street and stuck to the walls of this patio. "I feel like a firefly," she was going to say, but stopped at the thought of Aristeo's guffaw.

Then the patrona came.

"Would you like a room?"

She presented the great register, very greasy and crumpled. Isabel signed elaborately, minutely: Isabel Ayala, Widow of Díaz. Aristeo would have liked to sign himself, but remained quiet while the patrona asked:

"With two beds?"

"Naturally!" She felt like a superb actress. She gave Aristeo's head a studied maternal caress, and smiled: "He's a big boy now."

What fun it all was! She felt so gay and at ease. What delicious, perverse delight.

While they registered the patrona yelled:

"Angela! Get Number 7 ready."

They changed their clothes. Since it was the first night, Isabel decided they would eat out. But before they went out, they played around a long time, ran their hands over each other, but they didn't go to bed because Isabel wanted to prolong the excitement.

"Let's go eat, come on. Let's go eat first." Now playing the role of the young girl overcome with passion, giving Aristeo the role of the masterly lover and entertaining herself with the absurdity of the casting.

In the patio, she noticed the eyes that Angela was making at Aristeo.

"Aristeo, don't you want to ask the little girl to come with us?" Like an amiable aunt who wants her favorite little nephew to have friends.

"Ah, well . . . uh," Aristeo grumbled.

And they both went off howling with laughter, because Isabel's laugh was contagious.

A really clean cafe, crisscrossed by waiters in white and by the cool breeze from the fans.

"I've been here! It's 'La Parroquia'!"

It was. And everything had a special savor.

Later, the great discovery of the sea. There was a deformed moon which sparkled in the water. The constant splashing at their feet was a foreign language that made them feel they were in another country.

They walked slowly in the direction of the boarding house. They got lost, then they found it.

They picked up the key and a newspaper from the counter. It's the local paper. Let's see what it says."

The fragile door of their room closed after them. Isabel propped a chair against it and let herself be undressed by the boy. Their clothes stuck to their bodies and their skin smelled different, salty.

Afterward, with their senses satisfied, they were like two plants in a hothouse, submerged in a sweaty tranquility that seemed like ultimate happiness. This heat, this fullness, was the highest, most significant point in the time they had spent together.

The cold half-wakened her. It began as a vague discomfort that forced her to contract her muscles until they hurt. She huddled against Aristeo, but it was only a partial warmth that didn't suffice for her whole body. She heard strange sounds that terrified her. And warmth did not come.

Suddenly the window blew wide open with a violent slam. An enormous breath lashed across the bed, as if the world outside, the whole night, were falling on them.

"Aristeo, Aristeo. Go close the window."

But he didn't wake up. He turned over, didn't want to hear. The Norther had begun.

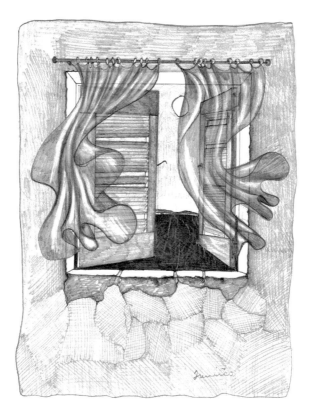

Chapter Thirteen

Aristeo had come in early in the morning. Isabel didn't open her eyes; she was aware of his taking off his clothes, without allowing that awareness to disturb the mist of the fragile and delicious somnolence which he penetrated almost immediately, possessing her. For that reason, now, contrary to habit, she didn't want to wake up although he was pacing around in the half light of the closed room.

He looked out at the street:

"What a hell of a day! Aren't you getting up?"

"Mmmm, no," and she turned over, fearing that he would let the light in. "Go look at the ocean, why don't you?"

He walked from one side to another, not saying a word. He

seemed restless, or something of the sort. Could the Norther be over?

"O.K. I'll be back after a while."

She listened to him leave and walk away. She could close her eyes and feel alone, deliciously alone. She went back to sleep. She heard quiet knocking at the door. She didn't want to wake, but there were the tiny, careful knocks of many little dwarfs. She opened her eyes, but the knocking continued. She put on her robe and slippers. She opened the door. It was Max.

"Oh, My God!" She wanted to run, hide, get herself cleaned up.

"Did I wake you?"

"No, I had already . . . Will you wait a minute? I look awful."

But he came in, as if he had understood that he would wait there, in the room. He seemed disconcerted.

"Didn't Aristeo come in last night?"

"Yes, it's just that . . ." That neatly made bed!—(they mussed it up every morning, to avoid suspicion)—and this man sticks his nose in unexpectedly. ". . . Aristeo straightened it up before he left."

"Straightened what? Oh, the bed." A curious smile. He sat down on the unrumpled spread. "I was afraid that . . . since I left him early . . ."

"Yes, he got in on time, but he went out a moment ago. Won't you excuse me a minute, Max?"

In command of herself once more, it was possible for her to address him so familiarly. She went out hastily, carrying some of her toilet articles.

When she came back, Max was stretched out on the bed, smoking. "Now how am I going to get dressed?"

Max, contrary to his custom, said nothing. He looked her over from head to toe, with an expression that made her uncomfortable. She finally sat down across from him and searched for something to talk about.

"And . . . have you finished your novel yet?"

"Almost. I lack a couple of hundred pages."

She was surprised:

"That's very long." Silence. "I've read a lot of novels." She could only remember the pornographic ones. She thought and thought, but the only things she could recall were forbidden pages, some with illustrations. She repeated weakly, "Lots of novels."

"What ones?"

Momentarily daunted, she ran through her entire library. Finally she murmured, with relief:

"The Three Musketeers." And blushed, as if she had said something gross.

Now Max seemed amused:

"A fine novel."

She felt as if she were transparent, and she herself incapable of even seeing his face.

"And . . . what is it you write about?"

"Sex, psychology. A little adventure à la Hemingway. Lots of sex."

"Ah."

Silence. He looked at her again with that kind of ironic curiosity.

"Are you cold?"

"No." He had noticed. "Why am I trembling, why?" It made her want to cry, but that went away when he spoke again.

"It was a pretty day, but it's getting cold again. Are you listening?"

"Yes."

"It's just that you're so far away. Come on over here, huh?"

Chapter Fourteen

They woke to a gray day, to feeble and malignant light. Breakfast in the dining room seemed sordid: the cups and plates made a loud noise, obvious perhaps because of the general silence.

They didn't really want to go out in the street, but neither did they want to stay inside. Outside another surprise was awaiting them; a fine, invisible drizzle that wet their faces almost immediately.

They walked to the jetty and the sea was frightening, bursting over the sidewalk, making puddles on the benches.

They went into a souvenir shop, to look at things. Out of boredom Isabel bought a tortoise comb. She didn't feel like talking, but Aristeo's ill-humored silence angered her.

"What would you like to buy?" She looked at the mean, calcified profusion. "There's nothing but dead animals in this shop."

Two enormous stuffed turtles with beady glass eyes; sea urchins, snails, star fish, sea horses; shells of all sizes and colors, some stuck together in the most abominable combinations.

"Look, this is a beaut, eh? For my old lady."

She paid for the comb and the box encrusted with snails. They went out again.

They got on a streetcar, so that they saw a lot of wooden balconies, houses with sandy patios, many grassy, stony streets, at the end of which they caught a small glimpse of the turbulent ocean. They paid twice and returned, finally, to the point at which they had begun. They watched the streetcar as it pulled away, shaking like a wet animal and clanging its bell in reprobation.

"Let's go eat."

That afternoon they went to a movie, and to a different one in the evening.

Once in bed, they made love unenthusiastically and almost died of cold until Aristeo got up and brought the covers from the unoccupied bed. The Norther made lugubrious noises and shook the shutters at the windows.

"Isn't this weather ever going to change?"

Angela smiled and held out hope:

"It will get better tomorrow."

It was a gray day, but it was no longer raining. A luke-
warm mist spread over everything, and no wind came to blow
it away.

"A day like yesterday." Walking through the streets, discovering parks and statues, ice-cream stands, cheap movie
houses. In the afternoon they went to see two more movies.
They went to bed early.

The next day, Aristeo was as restless as a bitch in heat.
"I don't want to go out, you go. But don't be late. I'm
going to stay here and embroider a little."

She watched him wind the cheap, ostentatious wrist watch
she had given him. She watched him leave. Then, she proceeded as if she were in her own home. She put on her
make-up with extreme care; she put on one of her new
dresses. She took her embroidery hoop and floss and went to
sit in a corner of the patio. Automatically, she resumed the
work interrupted in Mexico City. She knew that he would
didn't matter. She tried to put her finger on what was impor-
come back late. "I wonder if he's looking for women?" It
tant in their story, but she did not succeed. It was a simple,
immutable relationship, but it was difficult for her to visual-
ize its outcome. She didn't consciously rationalize the situation, but she was dissatisfied with its mechanical nature, its
lack of direction, their feeling of being suspended in a tepid
cloud..

"Aristeo . . . Aaa . . . ris . . . te . . . o. Aaa . . . riis . . . te . . .o . . ."
She accompanied the movements of the needle, until the
name was converted into four meaningless syllables. So,
thread by thread, she too was being emptied, until she was

one with the flat, geometric flowers: "Aaa . . . riis . . . te . . . o.
Aaa . . . ris . . . te . . . o . . ."

Short sentences formed in that meaningless symmetry, then disappeared, to the rhythm of the needle: "Now, green thread for the leaves . . . Aaa . . . riis . . . te . . . o . . . It's easier than taking it out . . . I hope he isn't late for dinner . . . Then, darker red threads . . . Aaa . . . riis . . . te . . . o . . . Aaa . . . riis . . . te . . . o . . ."

Chapter Fifteen

When he came to breakfast, Isabel wasn't there. Angela said
to him:

"Your aunt and your friend went for a walk together." And
she rocked on her tiptoes.

"Oh. Give me breakfast."

"It's too late now." She smiled, to observe the effect of
the following sentence, in a very special tone:

"*I'll* get it for you anyway, eh? Sit down."

Isabel walked around in inexplicable anguish, not realiz-
ing where she was going. She was ashamed to see Aristeo.
"He'll know," she thought. "Why *should* he know?"

Max had left with her, but she sent him away:

"Leave me alone, will you?" And she had gone on, not looking back, burdened with heavy shame and confused remorse.

She couldn't think straight. She looked for excuses: "We haven't promised each other anything. He must do the same thing." She wanted to find some consolation: "There's nothing to be sad about. It was very pleasant." No, it *hadn't* been pleasant. And she hurried her step, directionless, as if she were fleeing something, as if Max were going to overtake her and begin the whole thing over again.

"Pig, filthy old pig," and with these words came tears, as she continued almost running through the sandy, unfamiliar streets.

Later, Aristeo ate alone. He wasn't worried about anything, but Isabel's absence bothered him. "Old bitch, I wonder where she is?" In a few brief days, a routine had been established, and it had been *he*, until today, who had the power to break it.

As he was having dessert, Max arrived.

"Are you eating by yourself?"

"Yes. Isabel, um . . . she went out for a walk."

They went out together. Aristeo was silent, absorbed, and consequently he did not find Max's silence strange. They sat facing the ocean. Over at the pier a ship was emitting a thick, heavy smoke that fell to the waves and floated there a moment before it was scattered by the wind. Black smoke, gray water, black sky. It was cold.

"So what happened?"—Max.

"About what? Oh, about Havana? I don't know."

"No, about Isabel."

"What *about* Isabel?"

"Did she tell you?"

The sensation was akin to that of fear; something numbing spread through him. Here it came, the great weight hanging over one's head when he has seen the rope breaking, strand by strand.

"Did she tell me what?" He was prepared now.

"It wasn't my fault, or hers . . . I went to look for you, and she was getting up, in her dressing gown . . ."

Aristeo didn't hear the rest exactly, but throughout the entire recital the pornographic image of Max on top of Isabel stood out very clearly, as if he had seen it. This he hadn't expected, nor did he understand very well the effect it was having on him. There was a silence.

"Don't tell her I told you." Another silence. "Listen, the boat leaves tomorrow."

The boat! He landed the first blow on Max's mouth, calculating the place where he could do most damage. He savored the surprise and the little cry from the other. He hit him again. Max got up from the bench, dully. He started to defend himself. A group of urchins gathered around and added their cries to the spectacle:

"Give it to him, you bastard!"

He had given it to him! He walked away, rubbing his chin, which hurt a little. Isabel and Max. As soon as he entered, he saw the half open door. Isabel was there.

They didn't say a word. He struck her on the face, he twisted her arm, he threw her on the floor, all in silence, breathing heavily. In reality, there was nothing more to say.

"You old whore."

He kicked her; and then she screamed, and *he* felt the pain clearly, a sharp pain, unknown, physical. As if he himself had cried out.

He ran out, terribly shaken, because he couldn't stand to see her like that. Angela was in the street. He went toward her, slowly.

"Hey, are you sick?"

"Come on, you, let's go to a movie."

(How strange his voice sounded.) Because there, at the window, the corner of a shade had moved. He put his arm around the girl's waist, not noticing her giggles, or her protests. He saw only that shade, in his mind's eye. The shade fell.

He released the girl.

"I'm going now."

And he walked away, without explanation, like a drunk, unable to see clearly where he was placing his feet.

Isabel packed everything, and each object evoked a sob and a cry. "Aristeo, Aristeo"; each repetition brought back scenes, gestures. She kept going over the whole story; it filled her, filled her entire life—the dark years with the General, the future years in her empty house. Because now she was going to wait for him, with the stubborn sureness of one who awaits that which will not arrive.

All his things were there, on the bed, plus a return ticket

and some money. When he arrived there would be nothing else in the room. "But will he come back to the room?" How would he find out that she had already gone?

The box covered with shells: a sob. His new suit, almost a cry. She wiped her nose, and dried her swollen cheeks. If only the mark at least of the blows would last forever.

Suddenly, inexplicably, it was night. He was tired; he felt like vomiting. He heard the sound of a siren, and realized that he was cold. He looked around: cargo ships, rope, shapes beneath pieces of canvas. He began to walk.

He came to the narrow path at the end of the breakwater. He had been in the dark for so long that he could see very plainly. The sea was no longer black; it was a new, thick color, lustrous, seething with palpitations and unexpected movements. He saw a few stars and many clouds. Walking, he counted the beacons: one, two, three . . . there were seven. He watched the circling beam of the nearest light; it passed over his head. So fast! It ran toward the horizon, did not reach it, returned. And there, where it originated, a spark marked the completion of each circle. He stumbled several times because he was walking with his face turned toward the sky. He thought he heard a sound that corresponded to the light of the beacon; he listened to it; more than imagining it, he listened with his skin, with his stomach. A long, piercing note, as from a high-speed saw, for the circular track, and a little crystal bell for the spark. He tried to make the sound with his mouth; no, that wasn't it. He looked, and listened to it, again. A great wave broke over him and he yelled. He stood rooted there, streaming water, shouting and laughing;

he wiped his wet hair from his eyes, pounded his drenched body, licked the salt from his lips. Never had he been so alone. He was at the brink of perceiving something that was not yet clear; rather, he desired it intensely. The image of Isabel came to him; indignant, he rejected it. He rejected, too, his home and everything he had known. Water continued streaming from him; he was sobbing, and desiring something he could not put into words. He was aware only of his own soaked body, of the tossing of the sea, of the colors of the sky, of the icy water. He was himself, master of himself, his mouth and eyes smarting from the salt.

He began to run, jumping over pools of water, toward the lighthouse.

The American Exploration and Travel Series
[COMPLETE LIST ON PAGE 141]

THE MISSOURI EXPEDITION 1818–1820

The Journal of Surgeon John Gale

THE
MISSOURI
EXPEDITION
1818-1820

The Journal of Surgeon John Gale
With Related Documents

Edited, and with an Introduction, by
ROGER L. NICHOLS

NORMAN
UNIVERSITY OF OKLAHOMA PRESS

By ROGER L. NICHOLS

General Henry Atkinson: A Western Military Career (Norman, 1965)

The Missouri Expedition 1818–1820: The Journal of Surgeon John Gale (editor) (Norman, 1969)

Library of Congress Catalog Card Number: 69–10623

Copyright 1969 by the University of Oklahoma Press, Publishing Division of the University. Composed and printed at Norman, Oklahoma, U.S.A., by the University of Oklahoma Press. First edition.

To Professor Vernon Carstensen, with thanks
for stimulation, help, and friendship

Editor's Introduction

THE SPECTACULAR SUCCESS of Lewis and Clark in 1804–1806 stimulated widespread interest in the area west of the Mississippi River. This interest, however, was not translated into action until after the War of 1812. During the years of rampant nationalism immediately following that conflict, many American leaders looked to the trans-Mississippi West as an area of strategic importance. As early as 1815, Secretary of War James Monroe proposed establishing a string of army posts on the upper Mississippi near Canada. Less than a year later Missouri Territorial Governor William Clark suggested that an army post be built on the Platte. While these recommendations brought no immediate action, they demonstrate a growing concern with western expansion and frontier defense.[1]

Repeated clashes between American fur traders and the Plains Indians further stimulated interest and lent a sense of urgency to demands that the United States government consolidate its control in the West. These factors led to support for military penetration and, in particular, for building army posts in that area. Editorials, memorials, and speeches echoed a familiar refrain: The Indian attacks resulted from British instigation; therefore, the need was clear—"End British domination of the American West!" Secretary of War John C. Calhoun conceived the idea of

[1] Edgar B. Wesley, "A Still Larger View of the So-Called Yellowstone Expedition," *North Dakota Historical Quarterly*, Vol. V (July, 1931), 219–20 (hereafter *NDHQ*).

an army post at the mouth of the Yellowstone River in western North Dakota and, in March, 1818, ordered the army to carry out this idea.[2] Because Calhoun wanted a fort on the Yellowstone, the resulting troop movement became known as the Yellowstone Expedition. This title, however, fails to describe accurately either what Calhoun had in mind or what was actually done.

After he learned that it was too late in the year to get any troops as far as the Yellowstone, Calhoun altered his original plan. He suggested building an intermediate post either at the Mandan Indian villages in North Dakota or near Council Bluffs in Nebraska. A few weeks later he decided that a post at the juncture of the St. Peters and Mississippi rivers and another on the St. Croix River were also necessary. Thus, by late 1818, Calhoun envisioned a cordon of forts stretching from Green Bay on the Great Lakes west to Montana to prevent further British infiltration into the northern areas of the United States. Calhoun's scheme became so far reaching and cumbersome that not one but three expeditions resulted. What was to have been the Yellowstone Expedition became the Missouri Expedition, the Mississippi Expedition, and a Scientific Expedition commanded by Major Stephen H. Long.[3] Unfortunately, the newspaper editors of the day never clearly understood this fragmentation. They continued to refer to all three troop movements as the Yellowstone Expedition, which after the autumn of 1818 had ceased to exist.

The journal and other papers in this volume describe what contemporaries called the "Military Branch" of the Yellowstone Expedition—what is more accurately called the Missouri Expedition—comprising a four-part troop movement in 1818 and 1819. Late in the summer of 1818, one battalion—half of the Rifle Regiment—traveled up the Missouri River to an island above Leavenworth, Kansas, where a temporary camp was built.

2 Hiram M. Chittenden, *The American Fur Trade of the Far West*, II, 562–65; Roger L. Nichols, *General Henry Atkinson*, 47–48.

3 Richard G. Wood, *Stephen Harriman Long*, 62; Wesley, "A Still Larger View," *NDHQ*, Vol. V (July, 1931), 220–21; Nichols, *General Atkinson*, 48.

Early the following year, the Sixth Infantry Regiment received orders to travel from Plattsburg, New York, to St. Louis, Missouri. From there the infantry and the rest of the riflemen moved up the Missouri to meet their comrades. Then the expedition, which included approximately eleven hundred men of the two regiments, continued up the river to Council Bluffs at present Fort Calhoun, Nebraska.

Council Bluffs was to have been a temporary stopping point, for Calhoun expected the troops to continue their ascent of the Missouri the following year. But, because of the Panic of 1819, charges of mismanagement leveled at the contractors, and political opposition to Calhoun, Congress refused to appropriate any more money. Therefore, the Missouri Expedition ended in late 1819 when the troops unloaded their boats near Council Bluffs.[4]

Usually commanding officers of all military or exploring parties dispatched by the United States government received instructions to keep a diary or journal account of their experiences. Apparently in response to such orders, one junior officer kept notes for this journal.

The author patterned his commentary on the earlier account kept by Lewis and Clark. In places his prose shows that he referred to their chronicle, and in others he practically copied their information, as examples cited in the notes indicate. In spite of this, the journal is fascinating reading, although it sometimes presents choppy, often fragmented descriptions. It recaptures the colorful and exciting, yet drab and grinding, effort to move men and supplies up the Missouri River.

From this account the reader becomes more aware of the transportation difficulties encountered by frontier Americans. Keelboating on the Missouri River was dangerous work. Sandbars, underwater snags, and floating trees caused accidents and delay. In addition, the strong current limited movement to a mere nine

4 Wesley, "A Still Larger View," *NDHQ*, Vol. V (July, 1931), 228–30; Chittenden, *American Fur Trade*, II, 567–69.

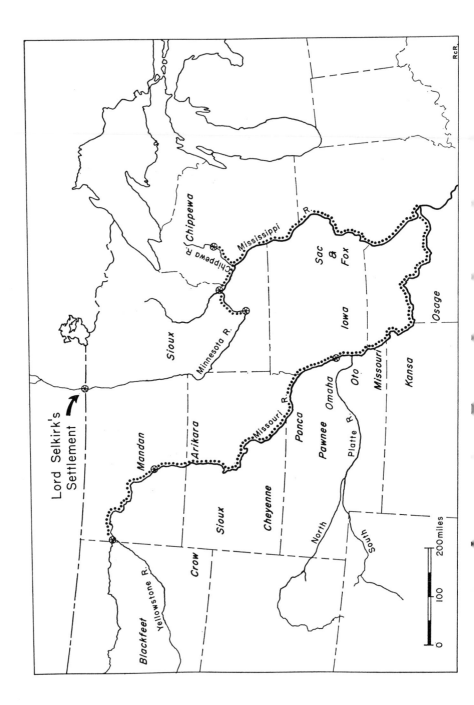

Lord Selkirk's
Settlement

Chippewa

Chippewa R.

Mississippi R.

Sac & Fox

Iowa

Osage

Kansa

Missouri

Sioux

Minnesota R.

Missouri R.

Ponca

Pawnee

Omaha

Oto

Platte R.

Mandan

Arikara

Sioux

Cheyenne

North

South

Crow

Blackfeet

Yellowstone R.

0   100   200 miles

RcR

miles a day. During 1819, when the troops had both keelboats and steamboats, their speed was no better. The sand and silt in the river water clogged the boilers of the steamers, while the current and snags slowed the boats.

The narrative also presents a stark and unpleasant description of army life during the early nineteenth century. The troops lacked good diet, adequate shelter, or any time for recreation. The enlisted men, in particular, suffered. In addition to their regular duties, they had to pull and pole the boats up the Missouri. Under such conditions it is not surprising that morale was low. The journal records several ways in which they indicated their displeasure. Many deserted, taking equipment and horses when they left; others committed suicide. Even the officers showed their dissatisfaction, some by dueling and others by resigning their commissions during the expedition.

This account also indicates why Secretary of War John Calhoun had been worried about choosing a competent man to lead the expedition. He wanted to impress the Missouri Valley Indians with the strength and good intentions of the government. In this effort the expedition failed, largely because Indian depredations destroyed any possibility of attaining the goals of mutual peace and respect. In fact, when it became apparent to the Indians that the military authorities could not stop them, the warriors became so bold that they tried to steal equipment and horses from the camp itself.

Some insights into the problems of diet, health, and medical practice in the army are gained from the narrative. For example, when the unbalanced army diet caused an outbreak of scurvy, the medical officers showed that they knew both how to prevent and how to cure the malady. Unfortunately, they lacked the food and medicine to do so. On the other hand, the doctors successfully treated gunshot and stab wounds and performed such major operations as leg amputations.

This record is of value because it describes the first sizable government-sponsored expedition up the Missouri River after

Lewis and Clark. Therefore, it provides the basis for comparing the extent and nature of settlement in the Missouri Valley during the sixteen-year interval between the two expeditions. From such a comparison it is clear that settlement had spread at least one hundred miles farther west than it had been in 1804. With this advance came the related and inevitable retreat of the Indian tribes. It is also possible to see the extent to which the early settlers recognized and exploited the available natural resources. Entrepreneurs, using primitive methods, produced salt, saltpeter, and coal. Some settlers used the rich bottom land of the river for farming or livestock raising, while other pioneers developed millsites and ferry crossings, all prior to 1818.

The journal makes it quite plain that this nation has not always had a vast, well-equipped military establishment or a powerful federal government. In 1818 the army was so weak that it could protect neither its men nor its equipment from small bands of thieving Indians. What is more, after a robbery or an assault, it had no way to apprehend the culprits. The government, too, lacked authority. It could not compel private contractors to provide the food and transportation which they had promised and for which they had been paid. Finally, the lines of supply and communication in frontier areas were tenuous and unreliable.

This journal has been considered the work of First Lieutenant Thomas W. Kavanaugh. A handwritten statement on the inside of the cover reads, "Kept in the main by Lieut Thomas Kavanaugh of the *Forsyth.*" According to Mr. Archibald Hanna, curator of the Western Americana Collection at Yale University Library, the library has no additional information about the authorship of the manuscript. In fact, the published description of this document seems to have been taken from the same source.[5]

It is true that Lieutenant Kavanaugh participated in the expedition and that he commanded the keelboat *Forsyth*, but there are several reasons for questioning his part in keeping the journal.

5 Archibald Hanna to Roger Nichols, Feb. 15, 1965; Mary C. Withington (comp.), *A Catalogue of Manuscripts . . . of Western Americana*, 7.

First, the statement attributing it to Kavanaugh must have been written by someone who did not write in the journal, for the script does not match any part of the original. Second, the name of the keelboat, *Forsyth*, is underlined—something not done in the manuscript. Third, the cover note suggests reading the Edwin James account of Stephen H. Long's Scientific Expedition to supplement this journal. The Long narrative was not published until 1823; therefore, the note was written some years after the Missouri Expedition ended. Finally, Kavanaugh died in May, 1823, probably before he could have seen James's book. This evidence certainly weakens the authority upon which Kavanaugh's authorship rests.

The journal prose indicates that it was written by a man with some scientific or medical education. This, Kavanaugh lacked. He was born in Clarke County, Kentucky, in 1799. As a boy of fifteen he became the deputy to the clerk of the Kentucky Court of Appeals in Frankfort. When young Kavanaugh was nineteen years old, he left the court clerk's office, obtained a commission in the army as second lieutenant, and thus came to participate in the Missouri Expedition.[6] The available biographical information fails to mention any secondary education, much less any medical study. Rather than scientific experience or education, Kavanaugh worked with legal documents and court records during the years before he entered the army. In the court clerk's office he would have acquired at least some of the legal jargon of the documents he handled, but no trace of such terminology appears in the journal. In spite of a slight similarity between Kavanaugh's handwriting and some of the journal script, Kavanaugh was probably too busy to have kept this record. He commanded one of the boats and later supervised the artillery, in addition to his regular company duties. Further, because there were so few officers with the expedition during 1818, increased battalion duties such as court-

6 Albert H. Redford, *Life and Times of H. H. Kavanaugh*, 51–52; Francis B. Heitman, *Historical Register and Dictionary of the United States Army*, I, 586 (hereafter Heitman, *Historical Register*).

martial boards, Officer of the Day, or Officer of the Guard certainly precluded his having much leisure time.

Perhaps more important is the fact that when small detachments left the main body of troops, the journal narrative often followed these detachments although Kavanaugh usually remained with the main expedition. Finally, the narrative contains a number of comments about Kavanaugh which obviously he did not write. For example, the November 4, 1818, entry includes the following: "The Magazine under the direction of that efficient and accomplished Officer Lt. Kavanaugh, was this day completed . . . ." At a time when formal and self-conscious prose was the rule, this sentence surely was the writing of a friend, and not of Kavanaugh himself. For these reasons, it is my contention that Lieutenant Thomas Kavanaugh is not the writer of this manuscript account.

In trying to determine who did keep the journal, one encounters many difficulties. There are some obvious and some less apparent changes in the script. They may be the result of several different officers' writing a part of the manuscript. On the other hand, they may be caused by changing quills or pens, by writing some entries when on the deck of a keelboat and others when on land. The most obvious method of determining authorship is to gather handwriting samples for each officer with the expedition and compare them with the manuscript. During 1818, ten officers were present, and the next year this number increased to thirty. It has not been possible to get handwriting samples for each of them during the time they participated in the expedition.

There is also a strong probability that the journal was written by a clerk from notes made each day. The clerks were usually enlisted men appointed for this duty, but no record of specific assignments exists. During 1818 there were about 340 enlisted men on the expedition, and the next year the number increased to at least 700. Obviously, there is no way to learn which of these men could write and then to get a sample of script for each. Therefore, although handwriting samples of Lieutenant Kavanaugh and some of the other officers present in 1818 have been examined, no positive identification of the journal author can be made using that method.

In order to determine who kept this record, one must examine the contents of the manuscript for internal evidence and logical inference. Both of these factors point to Surgeon John Gale of the Rifle Regiment. Unfortunately, there is little information available about Gale prior to his military service. He was born in New Hampshire, probably in 1795. Nothing specific remains about his immediate family, but the most complete history of the Gale family indicates that the four sons of Henry Gale of Weston, Massachusetts—Ephraim, Joshua, Henry, and Nathan—probably moved into New Hampshire during or immediately following the American Revolution. All traces of these young men vanish after 1781, when Nathan Gale, youngest of four, was discharged from the army. These four brothers are the only branch of the Gale family for which no record exists, and, since he is not included in the other branches of the family, it seems likely that John Gale was a son of one of them.[7]

John Gale began his army career as a surgeon's mate in July, 1812, when he was just seventeen years old. There is no evidence to indicate what, if any, education he had had prior to receiving his commission. Once on duty, however, he appears to have learned quickly, because by August, 1814, he had been promoted to the rank of surgeon. During the demobilization following the war, Gale, like most other officers, received a discharge. Within three months he had been reappointed to the Third Infantry at the reduced rank of surgeon's mate. In April, 1818, he was promoted to surgeon for the second time and was transferred to the Rifle Regiment in time to participate in the Missouri Expedition. Three years later Gale became a major surgeon, and, in 1830, he died at Fort Armstrong when only thirty-five.[8]

[7] George Gale, *The Gale Family Records in England and the United States . . .*, 58–59.

[8] Heitman, *Historical Register*, I, 443; Chandler E. Potter, *The Military History*

There is nothing within this brief résumé of his life to indicate that Gale had any college or medical school training, or even that he may have served some period of office training or apprenticeship under an established physician. Apparently he obtained his medical experience on the job during the War of 1812 and then read to enlarge his knowledge. It cannot, therefore, be said with any degree of certainty that Gale had the necessary educational background to have written this journal, but there is much evidence within the account which points to him as the principal author.

One of the clearest indications is found when small detachments left the main body of troops. In every instance when Gale accompanied these detachments, the journal either describes their activity or includes almost nothing about events at the main camp. For example, on October 13, 1818, Gale and Lieutenant James Gray, the regimental quartermaster, traveled ahead of the rest of the expedition to choose several likely sites for the winter encampment. The narrative follows their detachment as it preceded the expedition. In addition, the prose includes the first-person pronouns "we" and "us" in describing the detachment and the third-person pronoun "they" when the detachment rejoined the main portion of the expedition. It is clear, therefore, that one of these two officers was writing the journal or at least was keeping the notes from which it would later be copied. This conclusion is significant because there is no change in content or script of the manuscript, which means that the person who was keeping the record also made the earlier entries. Since Lieutenant Gray had joined the expedition only five days previously, Dr. Gale was the only officer who could have been keeping the account.

Another indication of Gale's authorship is found in the March 31, 1819, entry. There he noted that a separate record of weather information would be kept. This notation was in response to an

---

of the State of New Hampshire, Part II, 35–36, 59; *St. Louis Beacon*, August 12, 1830; *Missouri Republican*, August 10, 1830.

order from Surgeon General Joseph Lovell in 1818 that beginning on January 1, 1819, each regimental and post surgeon
had to submit quarterly reports, which were to include a discussion of sickness, medical activity, and specific weather information. The first quarterly report had to be written on or soon
after March 31, 1819. Gale did include the desired information
in his reports, and the remainder of the journal contains only a
few incidental references to the weather. There is no reason why
anyone except the medical officer should mention the separate
weather record here.

The frequent comments on health, diet, and injuries suggest
that a medical officer was keeping this record. For example, the
narrative describes gunshot and stab wounds and includes such
information as the location and seriousness of the injury, as well
as the length of time the injured man would be incapacitated.
These comments provide ample proof that the writer had some
knowledge of medicine and of anatomy, as is noted in the text.

In January, 1820, the journal narrative stops temporarily, and
the blank pages are used as a letter book for Gale's medical correspondence with the camp and regimental commanders. There
are eleven letters in this section. Most of them were copied by a
clerk, but a few are in Gale's own script, which is evident when
these letters are compared with other samples of his writing. If
Lieutenant Kavanaugh had been keeping the journal, there
would have been no reason for the narrative to cease or for Gale's
letters to appear. Between January and April, 1820, only a few
entries were made. Because Gale was so busy treating sick and
dying soldiers during the massive outbreak of scurvy which swept
the camp during those months, he probably found little time to
keep the journal.

In May, 1823, Lieutenant Kavanaugh died while en route to
his home in Kentucky. Had this journal been his property or
work, it would undoubtedly have been sent to his family with
his other personal effects. The journal remained, however, with
Dr. Gale. In 1827 he became the post surgeon at Jefferson Bar-

racks near St. Louis, and in July, 1830, he died while still serving in that capacity.[9] The last three pages in the manuscript contain an inventory of ward equipment and supplies at the hospital, apparently taken by Gale's successor in September, 1830. This notation shows that Gale had the manuscript in his possession and that even after his death it had remained with his papers in the hospital office.

To draw together this evidence, one need only consider the general continuity of thought and expression within the manuscript. True, there are several different handwritings with minor differences in spelling, punctuation, and grammar, but no more than might occur if several different clerks copied Gale's notes or wrote from his dictation.

Beyond the internal evidence, there are several inferences which can be drawn after a careful reading of the journal. As a surgeon, Dr. Gale would have had an interest in the medical and scientific aspects of the expedition. The many comments on minerals, fish and game, and vegetation indicate some knowledge of the natural sciences. It is more likely that Gale would have included this kind of information rather than Kavanaugh, a former clerk.

In addition, Gale had more opportunity than any of the regular company officers to keep such a journal. Unlike Lieutenant Kavanaugh, he had no boat to command or troops to inspect during the upriver journey. Also, as regimental surgeon he usually had an assistant or clerk to help him treat injured soldiers and to keep the medical records. The possibility that his clerks wrote the final copy of the manuscript would help to explain the different scripts within the journal and some of the obvious copying errors noted in the text.

Another conclusion may be drawn from the sort of non-military and detached attitude evident in places within the narrative. Not only is there little mention of specific military activities, but also training and procedures are discussed as if the

9 Heitman, *Historical Register*, I, 443.

writer had no part in the activity. This attitude is certainly closer to the position occupied by the surgeon than by a regimental officer personally involved in the training, command, or disciplinary activities.

The probability that Gale is the author is enhanced by the fact that as the regimental surgeon he had the responsibility of determining the cause of death for each fatality which occurred during the expedition. While such information might be considered important enough to be included by anyone keeping the journal, Gale would have been more likely than others to have included it.

From the internal evidence and the inferences discussed above, it is clear that Dr. John Gale, and not Lieutenant Thomas Kavanaugh, wrote most or all of this journal.

To supplement the journal manuscript, this volume contains certain letters and military orders, which have been included to fill gaps in the expedition narrative. When Colonel Henry Atkinson received orders to move the Sixth Infantry west and take command of the Missouri Expedition, he was also told to keep a record of his activities.[10] Either he ignored this order or else this manuscript has been lost. Therefore, in order to follow the movement of half of the expedition, some of Atkinson's letters and orders are necessary. They trace his progress from Plattsburg, New York, to Pittsburgh and down the Ohio River to St. Louis. In addition, they describe moving the rest of the riflemen up the Missouri with the Sixth Infantry in 1819. A few other related items have also been included, but no effort has been made to present all the documents relating to this move.

The original text and syntax of the Gale journal and other documents have been retained with only minor changes. A few missing capital letters and periods have been added, and extraneous dashes following periods have been deleted. Frequent errors in spelling, punctuation, grammar, and capitalization

10 John C. Calhoun to Henry Atkinson, March 27, 1819 (see Appendix, item # 5.)

made within sentences stand unchanged. The spelling of the names of people or places identified in the notes has been corrected there. The date entries are given in full rather than as abbreviated in the manuscript, and the day of the week has been added to each date. The number of each page of the original manuscript is given in brackets at the point within the text where the page begins. For the convenience of the reader, the journal has been divided into parts or chapters. In the appended documents any repetitious or irrelevant material has been omitted, including the complimentary closes of the letters.

Various persons and institutions have aided with this project, and all have my deepest appreciation. Some deserve a special note of thanks: Mr. Archibald Hanna, curator of the Western Americana Collections at Yale University Library, arranged for the filming of the manuscript and helped secure permission to publish the journal. Mr. Elmer O. Parker, of the Army and Navy Branch of the National Archives; Mrs. Frances Stadler, archivist of the Missouri Historical Society in St. Louis; Mrs. Christine Burroughs, of the University of Georgia Library; Mrs. Elizabeth Jones, of the University of Georgia Map Library; Dr. W. Edwin Hemphill, editor of the South Caroliniana Library in Columbia, South Carolina; and Miss Ruth Davis and the staff of the State Historical Society of Wisconsin—all have helped provide material for identifying people and places in the journal.

Professor Harwood Hinton, editor of *Arizona and the West*, graciously read the manuscript and provided suggestions for improving the editorial techniques. Professor John Perrin, University of Oregon, aided by criticizing the introductory material. Thanks are also due to Mr. Savoie Lottinville, former director of the University of Oklahoma Press, for his interest and encouragement during the early stages of this project, and to the staff of the Press. The Office of General Research of the University of Georgia provided funds and a quarter of released time to complete this project, and the American Philosophical Society helped with the costs of travel and research away from home. My wife, Marilyn, provided the tranquil home environment which is necessary for successful research and writing, and she has typed the final copy of the manuscript. The mistakes are mine and appear in spite of the efforts of all concerned to present this as an error-free manuscript.

ROGER L. NICHOLS

Athens, Georgia
January, 1969

Contents

Illustrations

Maps

THE MISSOURI EXPEDITION 1818–1820
The Journal of Surgeon John Gale

PART I

Bellefontaine to Cow Island
1818

[1] In the Spring of 1818, it became apparent to the American government that the hostillities manifested by the Indian tribes against our defenceless frontiers had been excited by British emisaries. The Earl of Selkirk,[1] Hudson Bay, and North western furtrading companies[2] had formed establishments within the boundaries of the United States. Trading houses had by them been erected at every desirable point. Thus situated in the heart of our Indian country, with presents and fair speeches, these tools of a corrupt government, won the confidence of the unsophisticated Indians and excited in their breasts either contempt or hatred for the American name.[3]

For the purpose of annihilating this baneful influence, our executive conceived it advisable to throw a Military force into the Indian country competent to the dispersion of these usurpers of the rights of the American fur traders, and sufficiently power-

[1] Thomas Douglas, Fifth Earl of Selkirk (1771–1820). A Scotch nobleman who established a colony for highland Scots in the Red River Valley of Canada in 1812. Leslie Stephen and Sidney Lee (eds.), *Dictionary of National Bibliography*, XV, 350–53.

[2] The Hudson's Bay Company and the Northwest Company were the two major fur trading companies operating in Canada and the Rocky Mountains. In 1821 they merged.

[3] British and Canadian fur traders received permission to trade with Indians within the United States from Article III of the Treaty of London (Jay's Treaty) of 1794. Hunter Miller, ed., *Treaties and Other International Acts of the United States of America*, II, 246–48. The Indian Trade and Intercourse Act of 1816 ended this privilege. *U. S. Statutes at Large*, III, 332–33; Wesley, "A Still Larger View," *NDHQ*, Vol. V (July, 1931), 219–21.

ful to protect our infant, but rapidly increasing Settlements on the Missouri–a River falling into the Mississippi in Lat 38. North, Long from Greenwich 89. The land adjacent to which presents to the agriculturalist the most facinating alurements, and can by no country be surpassed in Salubrity of climate, richness and fertillity of Soil, and beauty of landscape, variegated by hill and dale, creek and river, every where abounding in Mineral and Salt Springs. Thus combining every thing desirable to the Farmer and Mechanic, it would not fail of attracting emigrants from every part of the Union. To protect and encourage whom, the Yellow Stone river falling into the Missouri in Lat 48 North, and Long 27, West from Washington 1800 Miles from its junction with the Mississippi, was conceived to be the most desirable point to form the contemplated Military establishment.

Accordingly Brig Genl Thos A Smith,[4] was vested with full powers to concentrate a body of troups sufficient to carry into operation the design of Government, to purchase and equip a fleet adequate to the transportation of the troops, and every thing required to the formation of a perminant Military post.

[2] That distinguished and accomplished Officer, Col Talbot Chambers,[5] with the 1st Battalion of the Rifle Regiment, was immediately selected for this enterprize, Who with all possible dispatch concentrated his forces at Belle Fontaine[6] near the Mouth of the Missouri. Where he awaited the necessary supplies of

[4] Colonel Thomas A. Smith, a brevet brigadier general, commanded the Rifle Regiment and also administered the Ninth Military Department which included Kentucky, Tennessee, and the area north of Arkansas and west of the Mississippi River. Smith resigned his commission in November, 1818, to accept the position of receiver of public monies at the federal land office in Franklin, Missouri Territory. Heitman, *Historical Register*, I, 903; Raphael P. Thian, *Some Notes Illustrating the Military Geography of the United States*, 48; Howard L. Conrad (ed.), *Encyclopedia of the History of Missouri*, VI, 9.

[5] Lieutenant Colonel Talbot Chambers was second in command of the Rifle Regiment. In November, 1818, he was promoted to colonel and given command of that unit. Heitman, *Historical Register*, I, 294.

[6] Fort or Cantonment Bellefontaine was built in 1805 on the south bank of the Missouri River four miles above its mouth. It served as a staging point for western army units until replaced by Jefferson Barracks in 1827. Francis P. Prucha, *Guide to the Military Posts of the United States*, 60.

ordnance Stores, and provisions, which in consequence of the lethargy of Government, and the unwarrented and unnecessary delays of Col Johnson[7] the contractor, did not arrive until the 30th of August, When the Ordnance Stores and provisions, calculated for the consumption of one Month, Was received.

Rendered impatient by the past unexpected delay, it was determined that the expidition should proceed, after receiving promises from the contractor that additional supplies should immediately follow. Thus with seven public boats, 347 Men, a boat commanded by Capt Mc Intosh[8] destined for Fort Osage,[9] a Sutlers,[10] and contractors boat containing one Months provision, was this hazardous and important enterprise commenced, in order as follows . . . .

Preliminary Arrangements

Each boat is calculated to carry 35 ton burden, rigged with oars, sails, anchors, and cordell ropes[11] which are indispensibly necessary to Stem a boat against the rapidity of the current. Each boat is armed with a four pound Howitz[er] on its bow, and carries an equal proportion of powder, other ordnance and Quarter Masters Stores, so that in case an accident should destroy one boat, a portion of each individual article may be preserved in

[7] James Johnson was the civilian businessman who received the supply and transportation contracts for the Missouri and Mississippi Expeditions from 1818 until 1820. Allen Johnson and Dumas Malone (eds.), *Dictionary of American Biography* (1946 ed.), X, 103 (hereafter *DAB*).

[8] Captain James S. McIntosh of the Rifle Regiment transferred to the Ordnance Department in September, 1818. Heitman, *Historical Register*, I, 669.

[9] Fort Osage was built in 1808 on the south bank of the Missouri near Sibley, Missouri. It was to protect the United States Factory or fur-trade post there. This is sometimes called Fort Clark in honor of William Clark, who chose the site and directed the building. Prucha, *Military Posts*, 96; William Clark, *Westward with Dragoons* (ed. by Kate L. Gregg), 6–9 (hereafter Gregg, *Westward with Dragoons*).

[10] The sutler was a civilian merchant operating a store or post exchange at army camps. He provided extra food and whisky as well as clothing and civilian goods.

[11] A cordelle or tow rope was used two ways. It was tied to the mast and some of the crew pulled the boat from the riverbank. Occasionally, one end was tied to a tree and the other was attached to a windlass or winch on the boat. Edwin James, *Account of an Expedition from Pittsburgh to the Rocky Mountains . . .* (ed. by R. G. Thwaites), I, 122 (hereafter Thwaites, *James Account*).

another. A Commissioned officer is arranged to each boat, whose duty it is to remain on deck during the time the flotilla is in motion. Twenty men are assigned to the extremity of a cordell rope, the other end of which is attached to the top of the mast and thus wind their course along the banks, draging after them the boat. Several pioneers proceed with axes and prepare their way.[12] Each boat preserves the distance of one hundred yards from the others. Thus—[3]

The First Battalion of the Rifle Regiment, under the command of Col Talbot Chambers in pursuance of an order from the War Department, on [Sunday] the 30th of August, 1818, left their encampment near Belle Fontaine, and proceeded up the Missouri River, In order as follows:

1st The Genl Smith	Commanded by	Col Chamb[ers]
2nd The Col Williams	"	Capt Martin[13]
3rd The Col Benton	"	Lt Fields[14]
4th The Genl Harrison	"	Lt Shade[15]
5th The Govr Shelby	"	Capt Magee[16]
6th The McGunnegle	"	Capt Riley[17]
7th The Forsyth	"	Lt Kavanaugh[18]
8th The Genl Jackson		
Sutlers	"	Capt O'Fallon, Sutler[19]
9th Contractor's	"	Mr Rogers—Contractors Agent[20]
10th Eliza	"	Capt McIntosh

12 This refers to soldiers assigned to cut or clear away obstructions along the riverbank so that the men pulling the cordelle could more easily do their task.

13 Captain Wyly Martin commanded a company in the First Battalion of the Rifle Regiment. Heitman, *Historical Register*, I, 693.

14 First Lieutenant Gabriel Field, Rifle Regiment. *Ibid.*, I, 419.

15 First Lieutenant William G. Shade, Rifle Regiment. Lieutenant Shade resigned his commission in November, 1818, and left the expedition. *Ibid.*, I, 876.

16 Captain Matthew J. Magee commanded a company in the First Battalion of the Rifle Regiment. *Ibid.*, I, 684.

17 Captain Bennet Riley commanded a company in the First Battalion of the Rifle Regiment. He received decorations for gallant conduct in both the Seminole and the Mexican War and remained in the army until his death in June, 1853. *Ibid.*, I, 831.

6

The expidition this day proceeded but four miles when they encamped for the night on the east bank of the River. Names of the Officers employed on this expidition:

Col Chambers
Capt Martin
Capt McIntosh
Capt Magee
Capt Riley
Lt Shade
Lt Fields
Lt Clark[21]
Lt Kavanaugh
Surgeon Gale[22]

No. of Officers,	No. of Men	Total
10	347	359[23]

August 31, 1818—Monday: Weather fair, wind west. Proceeded at Reveille. Past Jameses ferry[24] at 12 O clock. Made this day 8 miles. Encamped at night on the West side of the River.

[18] Second Lieutenant Thomas W. Kavanaugh, Rifle Regiment. This officer is supposed to have written most of the journal. *Ibid.*, I, 586.

[19] Captain John O'Fallon, a St. Louis businessman, was sutler for the Rifle Regiment in 1818. His brother Major Benjamin O'Fallon was then an Indian agent. To prevent confusion, the first name of each will be placed in brackets in the text. *Ibid.*, I, 756; *DAB*, XIII, 632–33.

[20] This may be Harrison G. Rogers. He lived in the Boonslick area in 1819. Eight years later he died in Oregon while exploring with Jedediah Smith. Dale Morgan, *Jedediah Smith and the Opening of the West*, 194–95. It may, on the other hand, be Thomas Rogers, a Boonville tavern keeper in 1817 and a member of the Territorial Assembly the next year. Louis Houck, *A History of Missouri*, III, 8, 61. If this Mr. Rogers is not one of these two, there is no evidence upon which to decide who he is. This individual served as an agent for contractor James Johnson from 1818 until 1820.

[21] First Lieutenant John Clark, Rifle Regiment. Clark died later during the expedition. Heitman, *Historical Register*, I, 304.

[22] Surgeon John Gale, Rifle Regiment. Dr. Gale is the author of most, if not all, of this account. *Ibid.*, I, 443.

[23] This figure includes the two civilians John O'Fallon and Mr. Rogers and is not an error.

[24] This is not mentioned in other travel narratives, although a ferry is shown on

September 1, 1818—Tuesday: Last night stormy, morning fair. Proceeded at Reveille. Past La Carbonier[25] a Coal Mine on the North Side at 8 O clock A. M. This day lost one man by desertion. Arrived at St. Charles,[26] a flourishing town on the North side of the River, 21 Miles from its confluence with the Mississippi at 4 O clock P. M. when we encamped for the night. Made 6 miles.

September 2, 1818—Wednesday: Morning pleasant. Col Chambers, Capt Magee, and Capt [John] O Fallon returned this Morning to Belle Fontaine. In consequence of which, the command devolved on Capt Martin who assumed it accordingly and proceeded on our expedition at 8 o'clock. Lt Clark also in consequence of the absence of Capt Magee assumed the command of the Shelby. Made this day but eight miles in consequence of taking the wrong channel. Encamped at 5 O clock on the South side of the River.

September 3, 1818—Thursday: [4] Proceeded at Reveille. Morning foggy—Wind fair. At 11 O clock hoisted Sail. Continued under Sail until One O clock when the wind fell. Weather Pleasant. Contractors boat came up with us at 2 O Clock, which had fallen 5 miles in the rear in consequence of the desertion of three of her crew composed of French Boatmen.[27] Land undulating, Soil luxuriant, timber ash. Passed this day a Cotton Field, and a peach Orchard, for both of which the Soil and Climate appears adapted. Made this day fifteen Miles. Encamped at 5 O clock on the South side of the River.

September 4, 1818—Friday: Morning foggy. Proceeded at

the Anthony Nau map of 1810. Zebulon M. Pike, *The Journals of Zebulon Montgomery Pike* . . . (ed. by Donald Jackson), I, 324 (hereafter Jackson, *Pike Journals*). The ferry was in the vicinity of Halls Ferry, St. Louis County, Missouri.

25 This was about five miles down river from St. Charles, Missouri.

26 St. Charles or *San Carlos del Misuri* was founded in 1769 by Louis Blanchette. Houck, *History of Missouri*, II, 79–80. By 1819 the town included about one hundred homes and businesses. Thwaites, *James Account*, I, 126–27.

27 There were no civilian employees on any of the army boats, but the sutler and contractor depended upon Frenchmen, usually from St. Charles or St. Louis, for their crews.

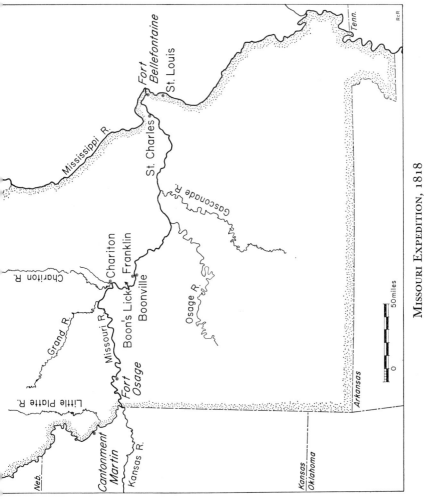

MISSOURI EXPEDITION, 1818

Fort Bellefontaine

St. Louis

St. Charles

Mississippi R.

Gasconade R.

Chariton

Franklin

Chariton R.

Boon's Lick

Boonville

Osage R.

Grand R.

Missouri R.

Fort Osage

Little Platte R.

Cantonment Martin

Kansas R.

Neb.

Kansas
Oklahoma

Arkansas

Tenn.

R.R.

50 miles

0

Reveille. Passd on the North Side Osage Woman River, on which is a flourishing American Settlement.[28] Passd at eleven Oclock a high Bluff of Rocks on the South Side of the river in which is a vast cave called the tavern[29] in which is carved on the rocks Many Names & Images amongst which are those of the celebrated Lewis and Clark[30] who first went on a Voyage of discovery to the source of the Missouri thence across the Rocky Mountains and down to the Columbian [Columbia] River to the Pacific Ocean during the years of 1804, 1805, & 1806. One Mile farther passd Tavern Creek[31] and encamped at the mouth of [one word illegible] Creek[32] on the South side having made eight Miles.

September 5, 1818—Saturday: Proceeded at day break. Passd several flourishing farms on each side of the River. Wind ahead. River has continued falling the last ten days. The Sutlers Boat came up last night which had fallen in the rear in consequence of the desertion of a part of her crew being reinforced by the Soldiers. The Boats this day separated for the first time, six passing up the South side four on the North. Came together at evening on the South Side where we encamped having made eight miles.

September 6, 1818—Sunday: Passed Wood River on the

[28] This stream is now Femme Osage Creek in St. Charles County, Missouri. Daniel M. Boone, a son of the famous Daniel Boone, established the first American settlement here in 1797. Houck, *History of Missouri*, II, 93–94.

[29] This cave is at the base of Tavern Rock, a bluff at the edge of the river. Lewis and Clark described it as 120 feet wide, 20 feet high, and 40 feet deep. Meriwether Lewis and William Clark, *History of the Expedition Under the Command of Lewis and Clark . . .* (ed. by Elliott Coues), I, 8 (hereafter Coues, *Lewis and Clark*). It was a well-known stopping place for travelers and perhaps was used as a tavern. Robert L. Ramsay, *The Place Names of Franklin County, Missouri*, 26, 36; Louis Houck (ed.), *The Spanish Regime in Missouri*, I, 183n.

[30] Lewis and Clark mention the cave, but say nothing about carving or writing their names in or near it. Coues, *Lewis and Clark*, I, 8; Meriwether Lewis and William Clark, *Original Journals of the Lewis and Clark Expedition* (ed. by R. G. Thwaites), I, 27 (hereafter Thwaites, *Original Journals*).

[31] Big and Little Tavern creeks merge and flow into the Missouri, one mile upstream from Tavern Rock.

[32] This is probably Labadie Creek in Franklin County, Missouri.

10

North,[33] and halted at 1 Oclock at a Village on the same side Called La Charrette.[34] Originally settled by the French, who have since removed to Osage River, it is now occupied by Americans. During our stay here, we had a fine Shower, after which the Wind Sprang up fair, and continued so until we had passed a very dificult pass immediately above the Village. In 1804 this was the highest White settlement on this River.[35] Made this day 10 Miles. Encamped at evening on the South Side.

September 7, 1818—Monday: Day pleasant. Wind West. Passed a Sugar [Maple] orchard on the South, also a Creek of considerable Magnitude.[36] A Sergt with two deserters came up with us from St. Louis at three Oclock. Progress much impeded by Sand bars. Several traders with a few Indians loaded with peltries passed us on their way to St. Louis. The River has been on the rise two days past. Our hunters this day brought in several turkeys and some buffaloe fish.[37] Made 8 Miles.

September 8, 1818—Tuesday: [5] Weather continues pleasant. Wind still ahead. Passed Shephards Creek[38] on the South West side, which is fifteen Miles in length, and eighty three distant up the Missouri from the Mississippi. At 4 Oclock arrived at Otters Island[39] ten miles in length narrow, Situated high, Very fertile,

33 This is a mistake, because Wood River joined the Missouri from the south. Apparently the writer confuses Wood River with two small, unnamed streams from the north. Coues, *Lewis and Clark*, I, 8; Patrick Gass, *A Journal of the Voyages and Travels of a Corps of Discovery* . . . , 14.

34 Fort *San Juan del Misuri* was established here during the 1790's. The village was near Marthasville, Warren County, Missouri. The residents left the original site because of floods. Houck, *History of Missouri*, II, 91–92.

35 Coues, *Lewis and Clark*, I, 9; Gass, *Journal*, 14.

36 This is what Lewis and Clark called Buffalo Creek, which entered the Missouri from the south behind Buffalo Island in present Franklin County. Coues, *Lewis and Clark*, I, 9.

37 The buffalo fish is a large ictiobine sucker and received its name because of its humped back. These fish grow up to three feet long and may weigh as much as fifty pounds. *Funk & Wagnalls New "Standard" Dictionary of the English Language* . . . , 348.

38 This is Big Berger Creek in Franklin County, Missouri.

39 Otter or Loutre Island was at the present Montgomery and Warren County line, near Hermann, Missouri. The first permanent settlement began in 1807 when

And is inhabited by several families from the States. On the North Side, three small creeks empty themselves. On the South Side, one, called Ash Creek,[40] twenty yards Wide. Timber on the bank of the River, principally cotton-wood, hickory Sycamore, and Ash. Encamped on the South Side opposite Otters Island, having made fifteen Miles.

September 9, 1818—Wednesday: Weather cloudy, wind fair. Made Gasconade River[41] at 12 Oclock. This River falls into the Missouri from the South 100 miles from the Mississippi—is 150 yards wide, & twenty feet deep at its mouth. Its course is through a rough country generally Northeast. On its banks are a number of Saltpetre caves.[42] Several American families are Settled up this river. Passed deer creek[43] on the South Side, four miles above the Gasconade and two miles farther Montbourns Tavern,[44] a cave on the North. Passed also Rush creek[45] on the South opposite a large Island. Land on the South Side appears fertile, covered with bushes hickory & other timber of considerable size. On the North land broken and rocky. Many bluffs of stupendious height meet the river. Wind continuing strong and fair. Made twenty Miles this day. One Sergt accidentally wounded by a shot.[46]

---

the McLain, Talbot, Cole, and Cooper families arrived. Houck, *History of Missouri,* III, 145, 154; *History of St. Charles, Montgomery, & Warren Counties, Missouri,* 752–54.

[40] This is now Frenê Creek, entering the Missouri at Hermann, Missouri.

[41] This stream joins the Missouri in Gasconade County, Missouri.

[42] Lewis and Clark mention similar caves. The saltpeter or potassium nitrate was found mixed with the soil. After separating the soil and mineral, the pioneers used the latter in making gunpowder. Coues, *Lewis and Clark,* I, 10; Joseph Thorpe, *Early Days in the West,* 24–25.

[43] This is probably Baileys Creek, which enters the Missouri at the village of Morrison, Gasconade County, Missouri.

[44] This lay between Little Tavern and Tavern creeks in Callaway County, Missouri. The name was spelled variously as Mombran, Monbrun, and Monbrains. It apparently came from that of Don Estaban Boucher de Mombrun, a French officer who served the Spanish. Ramsay, *Place Names,* 26; Coues, *Lewis and Clark,* I, 10; Thwaites, *Original Journals,* I, 36.

[45] This is present Dooling Creek. It joins the Missouri at Chamois, Missouri.

[46] This is the first recorded injury from the careless handling of personal weapons. There were many such accidents, because the soldiers carried ammuni-

September 10, 1818–Thursday: Raining last night and this morning. In consequence of which we did not proceed until 10 Oclock, When the Wind commenced blowing fair, but light. With the assistance of which and our oars, we were able to make head way against the current until three Oclock when the Wind failed. Proceeded by the aid of our cordell until evening when we encamped on a Small Island on the South Side. Made 12 Miles. Passed Big Muddy river,[47] coming in from the Northeast 50 yards wide at its Mouth, and 15 miles above the Gasconade. 3 Miles above passed little Muddy river[48] on the Same Side.

September 11, 1818—Friday: Morning rainy, no wind. Passed a large creek at 10 Oclock on the North side.[49] Soon after which we passed Bear Creek,[50] coming in from the South. About 3 Oclock Made the Grand Osage River,[51] coming into the Missouri from the South West, through a rich level country. The Osage at its Mouth is four hundred yards wide. Its junction with the Missouri is in latitude 38° 31′ 16″ and 133 miles from the Mississippi. Encamped nearly opposite the Mouth of the [6] Osage, on the North side at a French Village called Cotes Sanderslain.[52] The vegetable production in the Vicinity of this place, appear very luxuriant. American Settlements on the River Osage, and in the adjacent country are rapidly increasing. The Soil on both sides of the Missouri at this point is peculiarily adapted for cultivation. Made 9 Miles.

September 12, 1818—Saturday: Rains continue. Lost one man

tion on their persons and apparently fired their weapons whenever they felt like doing so.

47 This is Auxvasse Creek in Callaway County, Missouri.

48 This is Middle River in Callaway County, Missouri.

49 This is now Little Auxvasse Creek, one mile above Middle River and also in Callaway County.

50 This is Loose Creek in Osage County, Missouri.

51 The Osage River enters the Missouri at Dodds Island, Cole County, Missouri.

52 This is a misspelling of Côte Sans Dessein. Founded in 1808, it was the first white settlement in Callaway County, Missouri. The name came from that of a long, narrow hill just above the village. A flood destroyed the settlement during the 1840's. Ovid Bell, *Côte Sans Dessein: A History,* 9–10, 34–35.

by natural Death. After consigning the body to its Mother earth, with the usual Military honors, which engaged us until 10 Oclock, proceeded along the north bank which is Settled principally by Kentuckians. Southern bank broken. Encamped at Moreaus creek[53] 20 yds wide, coming in from the South. The river since last night has risen three feet. Capt Riley this day received a pistol Shot through the Neck, which will unfit him for active duty a few days.[54] Made 5 Miles.

September 13, 1818—Sunday: Clear Weather. Passed Cedar Island[55] early. Made Cedar Creek[56] coming in from the North, About one Oclock. This creek divides St. Charles, from Howard County. Timber on the North principally Cedar, which gives name to the above Mentioned Creek & Island. On the South Side, Hickory, elm, red oak, and ash. Some thistles, Grape Vine, and rushes. Our hunters saw Some bear this day, and killed a number of turkeys.[57] The small Islands appear white with gangs of Pelicans. Saw also a few geese. Made 12 Miles.

September 14, 1818—Monday: Morning pleasant. Wind ahead. Passed a rich level Country on the South covered with thistles, high nettle, and rushes. The hunters Killed three deer, and a few turkeys. Encamped on the South Side—back Country Settled. Made 10 miles.

September 15, 1818—Tuesday: Night and Morning Raining. In consequence of the continuence of the rain, and the wind being hard ahead Made but 6 Miles. Caught one deer near the

53 Now called Moreau River, this is midway between Osage City and Jefferson City in Cole County, Missouri.

54 There is no indication how Riley was shot or who was responsible. Note the medical comment about the seriousness of the wound.

55 Cedar Island was three miles long and covered with cedar trees. It lay between Moreau River and Jefferson City. Thwaites, *James Account*, I, 145.

56 This stream enters the Missouri about three miles above Jefferson City in Callaway County, Missouri. It is now a part of the Boone and Callaway County boundary.

57 The expedition apparently did not hire civilian hunters, but assigned soldiers to this task.

14

encampment in the River. Notwithstanding the heavy rain river fast falling.

September 16, 1818—Wednesday: Much rain fell last night. Morning cold and cloudy. Wind West. Notwithstanding which, we proceeded at 10 Oclock. Made four Miles and encamped on the North Side for the night, waiting for the Contractors boat, which in consequence of the high wind was unable to proceed until evening, When the Wind fell. Arrived at dark with the aid of a party of men which Capt Martin despatched to their assistance, under the command of Lieut Clark. River continues falling.

September 17, 1818—Thursday: [7] Morning clear and cold. Passed early this morning Rossia Purssia[58] a small creek coming in from the North, alias, Split Rock creek. Three Miles farther passed Saline River,[59] 30 yards wide, coming in from the South. Its name is taken from a number of Salt Springs & licks on its banks which makes the Water brackish. The hunters brought in three deer and some turkeys. Encamped on the North Side, at 4 Oclock. Lt Kavanaughs boat having grounded caused a delay. With the assistance of the aid however which Capt Martin sent him, he came up at dark safe.[60] One man deserted this evening. Made 8 Miles. River rising.

September 18, 1818—Friday: Morning Cloudy and cold. Passed big Manitou[61] a river coming in from the North, 30 yards wide. A little above which is a cavern entering a lime Stone Rock of a vast height, small at its Mouth, but Spacious within continuing one mile. From it issues a Stream of Clear Water, called

58 This is a misspelling of Roche Percée or split rock. The creek got its name from a perforated or split rock on a bluff near its junction with the Missouri in Boone County. It is now Perche Creek. Gregg, *Westward with Dragoons*, 52n.; Coues, *Lewis and Clark*, I, 16n.

59 The Petite Saline Creek enters the Missouri in Moniteau County, Missouri.

60 Here, as in several entries which mention Kavanaugh, the prose seems to indicate that someone else, perhaps a friend, is keeping the account.

61 Now Moniteau Creek, this joins the Missouri from the north at Rocheport, Missouri. It is not to be confused with Moniteau Creek on the south, about thirty miles down river in Moniteau County.

by the Neighboring inhabitants, Cold Spring.[62] An adventurous fellow entered without light or guide, and detained one of our boats an hour to extricate him. The adjacent rocks have on them several uncouth paintings, held in great reverence by the Indians.[63] In consequence of the delay occasioned by Capt McIntoshs boat runing on a Sand bar which required the aid of most of our men to extricate it from its then position, Made but 9 miles.

September 19, 1818—Saturday: Morning foggy and cold. Passed early good Woman river,[64] coming in from the North, 30 yards wide at its Mouth, navigable for boats Several leagues up. 3 Miles further arrived at Franklin a flourishing town on the North Side of the river.[65] Situated on an elevated plain containing one hundred Wood houses. Soil rich, Vegetable productions luxuriant, its banks are precarious composed of clay subject to be washed away by any change in the Missouri. Settled by emegrants from Tennessee and Kentucky. Opposite this is a Small town called Boonsville on the South Side.[66] Land undulating. Banks of the River lime Stone. These places are Situated 194 Miles from the Mouth of the Missouri. On landing a Salute was fired by the Inhabitants, from whom We received Many cortisies. Here we encamped for the night during which our band of Music[67] Seranaded the principal inhabitants. Genl. T. A. Smith our former

62 This is one of several small, unmarked streams within one mile of Moniteau Creek.

63 Lewis and Clark describe these rocks as "embellished, or at least covered, with uncouth paintings of animals and inscriptions." Coues, *Lewis and Clark*, I, 17.

64 Bonne Femme Creek enters the Missouri at Franklin Island, Howard County, Missouri.

65 Franklin was established in 1816 on the bottom land north of the Missouri and opposite Boonville. In 1828 most of the citizens moved two miles east to New Franklin because of river damage to the original settlement. Thwaites, *James Account*, I, 148–50; *History of Howard and Cooper Counties, Missouri* . . . , 166–69.

66 This town is south of the Missouri in Cooper County, Missouri. It was laid out in 1817 and was named in honor of Daniel Boone. *Howard and Cooper Counties*, 656; William F. Johnson, *History of Cooper County, Missouri*, 82.

67 This was the Rifle Regiment Band which included drum, fife, and bugle players.

distinguished Commander, had lately taken up his residence here. Made this day Six Miles.

September 20, 1818—Sunday: [8] The expidition delayed until 9 Oclock for the purpose of preparing despatches for the commanding Officer at Belle Fontaine.[68] Lieut Shade this day resigned his commission and returned to St. Louis, in consequence of which the command of Capt. Magees Company devolved on Lt. Clark. At the distance of six Miles, passed Mine river[69] on the South Seventy yards wide at its Mouth, and two hundred Miles distant from the junction of the Missouri with the Mississippi. The water of this river is clear, but rendered unpalatable by numerous rich Salt Springs on its banks, which gives the Water a brackish taste. Boats of any description can ascend it 60 or 70 Miles. The rich and beautiful Country adjacent to this river the distance of 40 Miles up is already Settled principally by emigrants from Kentucky. Passed a Short distance above this river and crossed to the North Side at a place called Coopers Ferry[70] where we encamped. Lost by desertion at different periods, eight men from the battalion Since it left Belle Fontaine. Several Frenchmen have also deserted from the crew of the Sutlers and Contractors boats. It appears by computation at this point that our flotilla has made an average distance of 9 Miles pr day. Made this day 6 miles.

September 21, 1818—Monday: Morning pleasant. Reached Arrow rock and a creek called Arrow Creek, and the prairies of Arrows[71] on the South at 4 Oclock. Opposite to which on the

[68] This apparently refers to the regimental commander Colonel Chambers, who left the expedition for Bellefontaine on September 2.

[69] The Lamine River is about six miles west of Boonville in Cooper County, Missouri.

[70] This was a short distance upstream from the Lamine River. The Coopers were among the earliest settlers in the area, but there is no evidence that they ever owned or operated the ferry mentioned. *Howard and Cooper Counties*, 656; Johnson, *Cooper County*, 82.

[71] Arrow Rock is at the state park of that name in Saline County, Missouri. Arrow Creek is Pierre Fleche Creek and now enters the Missouri about five river

North Side three Miles distant from the river are several rich Salt springs which are worked to great advantage. Near this point to the North is a creek[72] coming into the Missouri which takes its rise from an adjoining lake the waters of which are also impregnated with Salt. This portion of Country is called Boons lick.[73] Land on either Side of the river is high, rich and level elevated 50 and 100 feet above the water. The bed of the Missouri at this place is confined to a channel of 200 yards. At this place is a ferry Kept by a Mr Ferrel.[74] Three Miles above encamped on the North Side having Made 9 Miles.

September 22, 1818—Tuesday: Morning clear and pleasant, no wind. It is thought advisable by the Commanding Officer, Capt Martin, that in future the troops do not proceed until they have breakfasted. Previous to which hour the bushes are not only wet by the heavy dews which fall during the night, but the banks when Wet are so slippery that it is with much dificulty the cordell men can proceed along them. [9] Passed several Cotton and tobacco plantations on the North Side which appear flourishing. Red and White Roses of a beautiful description, large and small grapes, Mulberries, Gooseberries, Rasberries, and Several Species of a large White and Red plumb, every where adjacent to the River thrive spontaniously. Every plantation within our observation is surrounded by Cattle, Sheep, Horses, and hogs, the fine appearance of which evidences the fertility of the Soil. Passed

---

miles above the park. The Prairie of Arrows begins at the creek and extends north in Saline County. These names are supposed to be the result of the Indians' coming to the area to make arrow points from the hard rock there. Gregg, *Westward with Dragoons,* 53–54n.

72 This is Salt Creek in Howard County, Missouri.

73 The term refers both to the particular salt lick where Nathan and Daniel M. Boone gathered salt in 1807 and to the general area north and west of Franklin in Howard County. *Howard and Cooper Counties,* 149–50; John M. Peck, *Forty Years of Pioneer Life,* 134–35.

74 This was probably either John Ferrill or his son Henry. Both men trapped along the Missouri prior to 1817. Henry served in the Boone's Lick militia in 1812, and in 1817 was one of the first settlers to move south across the Missouri into the Miami Bottom area. *History of Saline County, Missouri . . . ,* 160; Houck, *History of Missouri,* III, 115.

18

hurricane creek[75] coming in from the north, a few miles above which we encamped having Made 9 Miles.

September 23, 1818—Wednesday: Morning pleasant. Passed on the North Side Greggs, and Bear Creeks.[76] Made two miles and encamped where we remained for the day for the purpose of giving our men rest and time to wash at a new flourishing town called Charaton.[77] Situated at the mouth of the two Charaton rivers,[78] which open together into the Missouri, 220 Miles from its junction with the Mississippi. The rivers are both navigable the distance of one hundred Miles from the Missouri. Land adjacent to them rich but uneven. Well timbered, and well watered. Large Quarries of Stone, numerous Salt and fresh Springs, a firm and elevated Situation, and an extensive rich back country, gives the town of Charaton a Superiority over almost any other Village on the Missouri. The inhabitants are industrious and enterprizing. Several Stone and brick houses, Flour and Saw Mills, constructed on the principle of an inclined plain are already commenced, and fast completing, Altho the first cabin was erected here, but one year since. We were received, and treated with Much courtisy by the inhabitants, Among whom are many families of distinction. This evening Made an excursion up the Charaton river on board the McGunnegle in company With a numerous assemblage of Gentlemen and Ladies, who returned at an early hour, highly gratified with the beauty of the Scenery and Music of the Band.

[75] This enters the Missouri one mile south of Glasgow in Howard County, Missouri.

[76] These creeks, about a mile apart, bracket the city of Glasgow. Greggs Creek is south and Bear Creek is north of the town.

[77] Now spelled Chariton, the town was two miles north of Glasgow in Chariton County, Missouri. It was founded in 1817. Two years later it had fifty houses and nearly five hundred inhabitants. During the 1830's the residents left because of repeated floods and malaria. *History of Howard and Chariton Counties, Missouri* . . . , 412–13; T. Berry Smith and Pearl S. Gehrig, *History of Chariton and Howard Counties, Missouri*, 216; Thwaites, *James Account*, I, 158.

[78] The East and West Chariton rivers merged and entered the Missouri at the mouth of the present Little Chariton River about one mile north of Glasgow.

September 24, 1818—Thursday: [10] Morning pleasant. No Wind. River falling. Proceeded at 12 Oclock. River difficult to navigate in consequence of numerous sand bars, planters, Sawyers,[79] and drifts of timber. Passed Several flourishing plantations, on either side of the river. Made 7 Miles and encamped on the North Side of the river.

September 25, 1818—Friday: Weather fair, but excessively hot. The banks of the river are high and falling in. Numerous sand bars, and drifts of timber, added to the rapidity of the current, renders our passage difficult and tedious. The Prairies at several points, Meet the River. They appear in general to be covered with Hazle, Grapevine, and plumb trees, destitute entirely of timber, but of rich Soil, and an undulating Surface. Passed plumb Creek[80] coming in from the South, near which a rich plain commences, of twenty or thirty Miles in extent, and of six Miles Width. Called the Miami Bottom.[81] Covered with Rushes, high Nettles grape and pea Vine, Elm, Ash, Hickory and Walnut timber. Made 7 Miles.

September 26, 1818—Saturday: Weather still pleasant. River fallen during the night to Such a degree, as to render it difficult to extricate our boats from the Sand bar near which we encamped. Came through Many difficult passes. Passed Round Bend creeks[82] coming in from the North between which is a

---

[79] A planter was a snag, log, or stump firmly embedded in the river bottom. A sawyer differed in that it was not fixed in place and that it could always be seen above the surface of the water. Both obstacles made river navigation hazardous. Coues, *Lewis and Clark*, I, 47n.

[80] This was probably Edmondson Creek in Saline County, Missouri.

[81] This was a rich bottom land south of the Missouri in Saline County, Missouri. It received this name because a band of the Miami Indians lived there. The first American settlement there was begun in 1817. Houck, *History of Missouri*, III, 122–23; *Saline County*, 158, 160.

[82] Several unmarked creeks flow into Cut-off Lake which was then part of the Missouri channel. From there they merge, becoming Palmer Creek, and join the Missouri about eight miles east of Grand River in Chariton County, Missouri.

large Prairie, Once the Seat of the Ancient Missouri Indians.[83] Made 3 Miles and encamped on the South Side.

September 27, 1818—Sunday: Morning Cloudy. At 9 Oclock Made the Mouth of Grand River[84] falling into the Missouri from the North 240 Miles from its junction with the Mississippi. 90 yds Wide at its Mouth, near which is a beautiful landscape of hill and dale. Passed Snake bluffs on the North a little above which we encamped at Snake creek, Alias, Mad river,[85] eighteen yards wide at its Mouth coming in from the north west. Made 9 Miles.

September 28, 1818—Monday: Morning cloudy. Troublesome drifts and Sand bars are numerous. Saw large gangs of Pelicans, Geese and Ducks. The hunters brought in two deer, and Several Turkeys. Capt [John] O Fallon joined us last evening from St Louis, and tomorrow will precede us to Fort Osage. Made 8 Miles.

September 29, 1818—Tuesday: [11] Morning pleasant, passed Tetesaw bottom[86] on the South. Six Miles wide, and twenty long, on which once stood the ancient Village of the Osages.[87] Mr Rogers the Contractors Agent has preceded us to Fort Osage, for

83 The Missouri are a Chiwere group of the Siouan family. They are closely allied or related to both the Iowa and the Oto. According to Hodge, by 1798 they had been conquered and dispersed by their enemies. Frederick W. Hodge (ed.), *Handbook of American Indians North of Mexico*, I, 911. This comment in the journal indicates that the writer had a copy of earlier travel narratives, because in 1804, Lewis and Clark had reported that "of this village there remains no vestige." Therefore, there could be no visible remains in 1818. Coues, *Lewis and Clark*, I, 22; Thwaites, *Original Journals*, I, 47.

84 This joins the Missouri three miles south of Brunswick and forms part of the boundary between Chariton and Carroll counties, Missouri.

85 The bluffs are near DeWitt, Carroll County, Missouri. The Snake or Mad River is now called Wakenda Creek and is south of the bluffs. Coues, *Lewis and Clark*, I, 25n; *History of Carroll County, Missouri* . . . , 213.

86 Teteseau Lake, west of Van Meter State Park in Saline County, Missouri, marks this area. The name resulted from an Anglicizing and shortening of the French *Petite Osage*, which pioneers pronounced Teet Saw. *Saline County*, 166; Houck, *History of Missouri*, III, 217.

87 This was about twenty-five miles upriver from the old Missouri village previously noted. The Osage were a Siouan tribe living along the Osage and Arkansas rivers. Coues, *Lewis and Clark*, I, 26; Hodge, *Handbook*, II, 156–58.

the purpose of procuring flour, and descending the River with it for the consumption of the troops who are nearly destitute. Made 6 Miles.[88]

September 30, 1818—Wednesday: Morning pleasant, Wind fair. Proceeded under sail all day. Made 10 Miles.

October 1, 1818—Thursday: Morning pleasant, Wind fair. Passed Tabo Creek[89] on the South 15 yards wide, and Tiger Creek[90] on the North 25 yards wide, near a large Island called Panthers Island.[91] Made 7 Miles.

October 2, 1818—Friday: Morning pleasant, Wind fair. Proceeded under Sail. Our hunters this day brought in two Panthers, Several deer, and some turkeys. Encamped a little above Eau Beau creeks[92] coming in from the South, on which are Several white Settlements. Land adjacent to the river at this point, high and Rocky from which issue many fine springs. Made 8 Miles.

October 3, 1818—Saturday: Morning clear and cold. Wind hard ahead, against which we were unable to proceed more than 3 Miles. Hunters this day brought in eight deer and a few turkeys. Saw some Bear. Four Indians joined us.

October 4, 1818—Sunday: Morning clear and Cold. Wind fair. Made 12 Miles and encamped at Fire Prairie Creek,[93] coming

88 The mileage figures for September 29–30 underestimate the present distance by at least fifteen miles. This difference may have been caused by shifts in the river channel.

89 This is also spelled Tabeau and Tabboe. It may have been Anglicized and shortened from *Terre Bonne* or good land. *History of Lafayette County, Missouri* . . . , 414. Or, it may be from Anglicizing the name Tabeau. Coues, *Lewis and Clark,* I, 27–28; Gregg, *Westward with Dragoons,* 31–32, 57n. The creek enters the Missouri about two miles west of Dover, LaFayette County, Missouri.

90 This is Crooked River in Ray County, Missouri.

91 This was on the south side of the river between Hicklin Lake and Lexington in LaFayette County, Missouri.

92 These are now Big and Little Sni-A-Bar Creeks east of Wellington, Missouri. Gregg, *Westward with Dragoons,* 57n., 58; Coues, *Lewis and Clark,* I, 29n.

93 This enters the Missouri about a mile west of Napoleon in LaFayette County, Missouri. Fire Prairie is supposed to have received this name because some Indians died there in a fire. Gregg, *Westward with Dragoons,* 57n.

22

into the Missouri from the South West, 300 miles from its junction with the Mississippi. At the Mouth of this creek we met with a encampment of 60 Kanzas Indians,[94] on their way to St Louis for the purpose of procuring arms, and Ammunition.

October 5, 1818—Monday: Morning pleasant, Without wind. Passed at three miles distance on the North, fishing Creek,[95] and at three miles further distant, Made Fort Osage, situated on an eminence on the South Side of the River, 70 or 80 feet above the level of the water, 306 Miles from the Mouth of the Missouri. This Fort which has perfect command of the River, which at this point is very narrow, was built in September 1808. Also at the Same time a Factory[96] was established for the purpose of trading with the Iowas,[97] Osages, and Kanzas.

October 6, 1818—Tuesday: Morning fair. Remained this day at this place for the purpose of altering our loading and cleansing the Boats.

October 7, 1818—Wednesday: Weather pleasant. Continued here this day for the purpose of collecting and loading the public corn, and other Vegetables destined for the use of the troops.

October 8, 1818—Thursday: [12] Remained at Fort Osage until 2 Oclock this day. Previous to our departure, Mr [Benjamin] O Fallon Indian Agent[98] arrived from St Louis, who is to

---

[94] The Kansa or Kansas Indians were a southwestern Siouan tribe. They lived near the mouth of the Kansas River and along the Missouri. They were guilty of frequent depredations upon traders and travelers. Hodge, *Handbook,* I, 653-55.

[95] This is now Fishing River in eastern Ray County, Missouri.

[96] A factory was a United States government owned and operated fur-trading post. They were used to control the trade and to insure fair prices and treatment for the Indians. They failed. For a complete study of this system, see Ora B. Peake, *A History of the United States Indian Factory System.*

[97] The Iowas were a southwestern Siouan tribe related to the Otos and Missouris. They lived along the Des Moines in Iowa, and along the Little Platte, Chariton, Grand, and Missouri rivers in Missouri. They were a farming and fur-trading people. Hodge, *Handbook,* I, 612-14.

[98] Benjamin O'Fallon was John's brother. He was the Indian agent for the tribes of the upper Missouri and also a member of the Missouri Fur Company. He is usually called Major while his brother is Captain. *DAB,* XIII, 631-32.

procede us, to our Wintering ground for the purpose of counseling with the Indians. Captain Gray[99] who previously Commanded at Fort Osage, this day gave up his Command to Capt McIntosh, and joined our Squadron, with twenty two of his men, whose places were supplied with 22 less efficient from the Flotilla. Doctor Clark,[100] Post Surgeon, also joined us from this place. The Contractors Agent who has been purchasing Cattle for the consumption of the troops, proceeds with them along the banks of the river. The Eliza, which Capt McIntosh commanded, is left at Fort Osage. Evening rainy. Made 3 Miles and encamped on the North Side of the River. Soon after which the corpse of one of our Men was discovered on the opposite bank of the River, who had deserted on the night of the 5th ultimo, having previously broken open the trunk of Capt Riley, and taken thence $100 Dollars in Silver. It appears by his, and the position of his gun, that he had committed Suicide by placing the Muzle of his Rifle under his chin, and thus blowing out his brains. He slept the night on which he deserted, about 1/4 of a Mile from camp in the rushes, where was left a blanket, Great coat, and other wearing apparel which he had Stolen. 4 Dollars in specie was found in his pocket. No traces of the remainder could be discovered. It is highly probable that being intoxicated when he deserted, he had lost the Money during the night, and in a fit of desperation, destroyed himself in the Morning.

October 9, 1818—Friday: Weather pleasant. Passed at the distance of three miles Haycabin and Sugar camp Creeks,[101] coming in from the South, six miles above Fort Osage. The latter is so called from a large Sugar [Maple] Orchard which grows on its banks. Land near the River, rich and well timbered for the dis-

---

99 First Lieutenant James S. Gray was then quartermaster for the Rifle Regiment. He became a captain in November, 1818, and perhaps knowledge of his impending promotion may explain why he is called captain. Otherwise, this is an error. Heitman, *Historical Register*, I, 472.

100 William J. Clarke was post surgeon at Fort Osage. *Ibid.*, I, 308.

101 Present Sugar Creek joins the Little Blue River, and they flow into the Missouri in Jackson County, Missouri.

tance of one half Mile, when the Prairie commences. Sand bars are numerous, covered with small willows. Our hunters brought in four deer, and Several turkey. Made 8 Miles.

October 10, 1818—Saturday: [13] Weather fair and warm. Passed a bank of Stone coal[102] on the North a little below which is a creek Called La Charbonier.[103] 4 Miles above is also a creek coming in from the South called La Benite,[104] a little above which we encamped having Made 5 Miles. Our hunters brought in a Bear and Several turkeys.

October 11, 1818—Sunday: Clear Weather. Passed some bluffs on the South 100 feet above high water Mark. The Prairies approach the river on both Sides. Parroquetts[105] are numerous. Our hunters killed Some deer, Geese & turkeys. Halted on an Island a little below the Mouth of Blue Water River,[106] where was a camp of Kansas Indians, who had collected and held a council yesterday with Mr [Benjamin] O Fallon, Indian Agent, who passed us at Fort Osage, and who still proceds us.

October 12, 1818—Monday: Clear Weather. Passed at the distance of 1/4 Mile Blue Water River coming in from the South 30 yards wide at its Mouth. A few miles up this River there are quarries of Plaster of Paris, [107] large quantities of which are yearly brought to St Louis. The channel of the Missouri at this point is very narrow. The Forsythe commanded by Lt Kava-

102 This refers to the layers of bituminous coal found in the limestone beds along the river here. *History of Clay and Platte Counties, Missouri . . .* , 14–15.

103 This is now Rush Creek in Clay County, Missouri.

104 This is Mill Creek in Jackson County, Missouri. The spelling is thought to be a corruption of the name Benoit. Coues, *Lewis and Clark*, I, 32n.; William Clark, *The Field Notes of Captain William Clark* (ed. by Ernest S. Osgood), 62n (hereafter, Osgood, *Field Notes*).

105 These birds were Louisiana parakeets. Their hearts were reputed to be poisonous. John J. Audubon, *Audubon's America . . .* (ed. by Donald C. Peattie), 148–49, 278, 280.

106 Blue River enters the Missouri at Independence, Missouri.

107 This is native gypsum. Processed plaster of Paris is a hemihydrate of calcium sulphate. *Webster's Third New International Dictionary of the English Language . . .* , 1733.

naugh, was this day pierced by a Snag through the Side, and before the aperture could be Stoped, took in Much water. Blankets were thrust through the hole, until the Boat was bailed, after which tared canvas with a board was Nailed over it, which effectually Secured it. Made 8 Miles. Encamped a little below the Mouth of the Kanzas River.[108]

October 13, 1818—Tuesday: Morning cloudy. Passed at a Short distance the Mouth of the Kanzas River, falling into the Missouri from the South West 340 Miles from its junction with the Mississippi 230 yards wide at its entrance, which is in Lat 38° 31′. Navigable nine hundred Miles up, it arises in a Prairie between the Arkansas and River Platte, and continuing its course through an open country until just before it enters the Missouri. The comparitive Specific gravities of the two Rivers, is for the Missouri 78° for the Kanzas 72° degrees. The water of the latter is clear, but of a disagreeable taste. A Tribe of Indians called the Kanzas, 350 in number reside 20 Leagues up this River.[109] The land on this River is of the first quality possessing a Variety of hill and dale. In pursuance of an Order from [14] Capt Martin, Lieut Gray Quarter Master, and Doctor Gale, Surgeon of the Rifle Regiment, preceded the Fleet this evening in the Genl Smith, for the purpose of selecting a secure harbour, and an eligible Situation for Winter Quarters. Left the Flotilla 5 Miles above the Kanzas River,[110] and encamped opposite the Mouth of the little River Platte[111] coming in from the North East. 60 yards wide at its Mouth the land on this River is of the first quality.

108 This enters the Missouri just west of the Missouri-Kansas boundary at Kansas City.

109 These descriptions of the river and the Indians seem to have been taken from Lewis and Clark. Coues, *Lewis and Clark*, I, 33–34.

110 From the wording of this entry it is clear that either Lieutenant Gray or Dr. Gale is keeping the journal. The writer stays away from the main body of troops until October 16, the day this detachment meets the rest of the expedition.

111 The Little Platte has shifted its course by fifteen to twenty miles. Apparently it entered the Missouri at Little Platte Bend, just west of Parkville in Platte County, Missouri. The present Platte River (of Missouri) enters the Missouri about four miles south of Fort Leavenworth, Kansas.

There are several falls on this River eligible for Mill seats. Made 9 Miles.

October 14, 1818—Wednesday: Morning rainy. At the distance of 6 miles made Diamond Island[112] opposite which on the North is a Stream Called biscuit creek.[113] Three miles above this Island, made three Islands, and a creek on the South called Remore.[114] 5 Miles farther made a cluster of Islands, two large, and two Small, called Field Islands,[115] at which we[116] encamped, having Made 14 Miles. Opposite these Islands is an extensive and high Prairie, approaching the river on the South, and on the North is a stream called Pare creek.[117]

October 15, 1818—Thursday: Morning clear & cold. Last night there was a Severe frost and some ice. At the distance of 5 miles passed Turkey creek[118] on the South, and at the distance of two Miles farther Made Bear Medicine Island,[119] on the North, at the extremity of which we encamped on the South in a Valley where once Stood the ancient Village of the Kanzas, a Mile in rear of which is the remains of a French Fort [120] which was Situated on an eminence near a Spring of fine water. The general outlines of

112 Diamond Island is about five miles above Kansas City and just north of Wyandotte County Lake in Kansas.

113 There are several unnamed creeks here. This may have been a branch of the Little Platte. Coues, *Lewis and Clark*, I, 36n.

114 This may come from the French *remora* (sucking fish) or *remous* (eddy or backwater). It is probably Little Snell Creek, which joins the Missouri at the southern tip of Stigers Island in Leavenworth County, Kansas. *Ibid.*, I, 36n.; Osgood, *Field Notes*, 64, 65n.

115 *Isles des parques*, Four Islands, or Field Islands are all used to designate this group. They were just south of Leavenworth, Kansas. Coues, *Lewis and Clark*, I, 36n.; Osgood, *Field Notes*, 66.

116 The use of the pronouns "we," "our," and "us" in the October 14–16 entries is clear proof that the journal is being kept by one of the advance party.

117 Sometimes given as Parque Creek, this is now Nine Mile, Seven Mile, or Five Mile Creek in Leavenworth County, Kansas.

118 This is either Three Mile or Coral Creek in Leavenworth County, Kansas.

119 Now Kickapoo Island in Platte County, Missouri, this is across from the Fort Leavenworth Military Reservation.

120 This was Fort Cavagnolle, built in the 1740's to protect the fur traders in that area. Osgood, *Field Notes*, 66n.

the works and the remains of the chimneys only are Visible. It was probably cut off by the Indians, since we have no accounts of it. Made 14 Miles.

October 16, 1818—Friday: Morning foggy. Made at the distance of three Miles, the lower point of Isle des Vatches,[121] which had been recommended as a suitable Situation for our encampment, and harbour. At this point, we found Capt [John] O Fallon, who had preceded us from Fort Osage, with our cattle and horses. At 2 Oclock returned despleased with the situation. The harbour not appearing safe, and the timber appearing unsuitable for building. Met the Fleet 10 Miles below, Near the lower point of Bear [Medicine] Island, 30 Miles above the river Kanzas, which they had made during the 4 last days.[122] Our hunters this day brought in several Turkeys & Geese, and 18 deer. The timber on the banks of the River appears to be Oak, Ash, Walnut, Hickory, Cotton wood, and some Paccaun.[123] The game appears More plenty, than it has been at any other point on the river, consisting of Elk, Deer, Bear, Beaver, Turkey, and water fowls.

October 17, 1818—Saturday: [15] Morning pleasant. Wind fair. Made 8 Miles and encamped on a point below Isle des Vatches. Our hunters brought in several deer, and a quantity of honey, with which the country abounds at every point between the Mouth of the Missouri and this place. Geese, and Sandhill Cranes, appear more numerous. The Banks of the river exhibit great sign of Beaver. Grapes, and a late species of Osage Plumb, are now in perfection, of which the Valleys both above and below the Old Kanzas Village produce large quantities.

October 18, 1818—Sunday: Morning cloudy. Made 2 Miles and encamped on an Island called Isle des Vatches (or Cow Island) Where it is designed to remain for the winter. This Island

121 Cow, or less frequently Buffalo, Island was in the vicinity of present Harpst Island at the Leavenworth and Atchison County line in Kansas.
122 Here is another indication that the writer has been with the advance party.
123 These are pecan trees.

is situated 380 Miles from the junction of the Missouri with the Mississippi. Our Flotilla has been 50 days on its passage to this place, having progressed at an average distance of 7, 3/5 of a Mile per day.

The command immediately on our arrival were directed to pitch their tents on the banks in a line parallel with the river, which was effected before evening. Under the cover of which our Men reposed for the first time Since the Commencement of the Expidition.[124]

[124] Apparently the troops slept on the boats or on the ground without shelter all the way up the Missouri.

PART II

Martin Cantonment at Cow Island
1818-1819

October 19, 1818—Monday: Morning pleasant. After detailing a Suitable Guard, the remainder of the Battalion were put in requisition[1] for the purpose of collecting materials for the erection of Winter Barracks. Captain Martin with a party went up the river in search of Stone, suitable for the construction of Chimneys, which he discovered near a bluff which approaches the river on the North Side two Miles above our Camp. The General Smith our smallest Boat was immediately unloaded, and the Music[2] dispatched to transport them to this place. A party sent out to make clapboards[3] from the Oak which grows on the opposite Side of the river to cover the buildings. Another party to make puncheons[4] from the Cotton Wood to floor them. A fourth party were sent to Manufacture charcoal, and a 5th party were employed in falling timber, and laying up the buildings. This evening unluckily a Soldier of Capt Rileys company in heedlessly passing a Sentinel, was Shot through the leg.

October 20, 1818–Tuesday: Morning warm and Smoky, assuming that appearance of weather which is usually denominated Indian Summer. Capt Martin this day found a bank of Clay on the Island near the camp, suitable to be used in building the chimneys, and Plastering the Barracks, which relieved us from

1 The troops were organized into work details to build the new camp.
2 This is the regimental band.
3 Clapboards were siding boards.
4 Split logs laid with the split or flat side up were used as flooring.

no little uneasiness. Our Cattle and horses which have been brought to the Island, with the exception of one horse which has Strayd, continue to thrive on the rushes which are numerous.

October 21, 22, 23, 24, 1818—Wednesday-Saturday: [16] The weather continues warm and pleasant. The buildings progress with rapidity which does honor to both Officers and Men.[5] Our hunters during the four last days have brought in a profusion of Game, and large quantities of honey.

October 25, 26, 1818—Sunday-Monday: Weather continues warm and smoky which proceeds from a fire which has taken on an adjacent Prairie in the South. Burnt Grass and leaves are continually falling about our Camp. The smoke in which we are enveloped so much excludes the rays of the Sun, as to render day almost doubtful. A boat arrived this day (26th) from St Louis bringing an additional Supply of goods to Capt. [John] O Fallon the Sutler, and a quantity of Indian Goods belonging to the Missouri Fur Company.[6] The Boat, after unloading the Goods destined for this place continued up the river to the Council Bluffs.[7]

October 27, 28, 1818—Tuesday-Wednesday: Indian Summer continues. The Prairies continue to burn and our camp still continues enveloped in Smoke. The Wind during the last ten days has prevailed from the South. The party at work on the buildings finished their erection this day (28th) and were immediately detached to commence covering and chinking them. The Officers have unanimously agreed to denominate the establishment Martins Cantonment.

5 Here is one example of the non-involved attitude which the writer shows on occasion.

6 This was the popular name for several St. Louis fur-trading organizations. The first of these was begun in 1808–1809. Chittenden, *American Fur Trade*, I, 137–50; Richard E. Oglesby, *Manuel Lisa and the Opening of the Missouri Fur Trade*, 65–149 *passim*.

7 Named Council Bluffs by Lewis and Clark after their meeting with leaders of the Oto and Missouri tribes there on August 3, 1804. It is at Fort Calhoun, Washington County, Nebraska. Coues, *Lewis and Clark*, I, 64–65.

October 29, 1818—Thursday: A trading boat from St Louis passd this day, which was boarded about 20 Miles above this by a party of the Kansas, who after plundering it of many Valuable articles, permitted it to continue its rout.[8]

October 30, 1818—Friday: Two men from St. Louis, arrived this day in a canoe, whose business is traping Beaver, along the Banks of the Missouri. They have already taken about 50.

October 31, 1818—Saturday: After inspecting the troops, Captain Martin, removed to his quarters, which are completed. The hills, Valleys, and Prairies are still on fire, the day is darkened with the Smoke, and the night illumined by the blaze. Mr Potts[9] the Sutlers Agent this day received a wound in the leg by the accidental discharge of a Pistol. The contractors Whiskey failed this day,[10] which compelled him to procure a quantity from Capt [John] O Fallon the Sutler. The weather continues warm and pleasant, which is favorable to our Workmen, who progress with great rapidity in the construction of Winter Quarters.

Isle Aux Vatches is about 2 Miles in length, and ¾ of a Mile in breadth, elevated 20 feet above the surface of the water, covered with cotton wood, Sycamore and Elm.

[17] [A one page diagram of Martin Cantonment]

8 This is the first of such depredations committed by the Indians upon the expedition. These incidents usually involved Kansas, Sac, or Pawnee braves.

9 There are many men with this name in Missouri at this time, and it is not possible to identify this individual. John Potts had been a private with Lewis and Clark and remained in Missouri. Thwaites, *Original Journals*, I, 11, 13; William Kennerly, *Persimmon Hill*, 157. Jonathan Potts had frequent dealings with Lisa, Lucas & Chouteau in 1817–19. Choteau Collections, The Missouri Historical Society, St. Louis (hereafter MHS). The information from this organization has been provided by Mrs. Frances H. Stadler, archivist. This could also be either Thomas S. Potts, Sr., an early settler in Jackson County, or his son. W. Z. Hickman. *History of Jackson County, Missouri*, 92. It may even have been Daniel T. Potts of later fur-trade prominence. Gerald C. Bagley, "Daniel T. Potts," *The Mountain Men and the Fur Trade of the Far West* (ed. by LeRoy R. Hafen), III, 249–62.

10 One gill or a half-cup of whisky was part of the daily food ration for each soldier. This comment indicates that the contractor had run out of whisky; therefore, it had to be purchased from the sutler. Erna Risch, *Quartermaster Support of the Army*, 203.

November 1, 1818—Sunday: [18] A boat of the Contractors which had been dispatched to Fort Osage for a depot of flour at that place, arrived this day. It appears that a party of the Kansas Indians, boarded them about twenty Miles below this, took from them a barrel of flour, and retreated with their plunder. Doctors Gale, & Clark, this day removed to their quarters which are finished. Our hunters bring in daily large quantities of Game. The Venison is very fat at this Season, but the Turkeys are lean, from the circumstance of their subsisting on Acorns which owing to their smooth surface, do not readily digest.

November 2, 1818—Monday: This day about 30 lodges of the Kansas Indians arrived on the Island, and encamped near our cantonment. It appears that they have been lately attacked by the Ottoes who defeated them, Killing a few, and taking Several prisoners.[11]
Their tents are composed of Buffaloe skins, fantastically painted. Their Children until about 8 years of Age, are interely destitute of dress. The Men in general have no other apparel, than a Buffaloe Skin thrown carelessly about them.

November 3, 1818—Tuesday: The Hospital Store was this day completed and the Sick removed to it. Also the Contractors, and Ordnance Stores were finished, into which the provisions, and the Articles appertaining to the Ordnance were removed.

November 4, 1818—Wednesday: The Magazine under the direction of that efficient and accomplished Officer Lieut Kavanaugh, was this day completed, into which our ammunition was removed.[12]

November 5, 1818–Thursday: The pieces of Artillery were this day removed from the boats, and Mounted in the Middle of the parade.

11 This is one of many journal references to the intermittent warfare among the Missouri Valley Indians.
12 Obviously this comment was not written by Kavanaugh, but by a friend.

November 6, 1818—Friday: Lieut Fields, and Quarter Master Gray with Capt Martins company, this day Moved to their quarters which are finished. A party of Socks arrived on the Island this day bearing offers of peace to the Kansas, who received them with open arms, and loud and repeated Shouts.[13] The appearance of the Socks is far Superior to any other tribe, which we have yet seen. The hairs are plucked from their heads, with the exception of a Small tuft which remains on the crown, and the scalp is fantastically painted.

November 7, 1818—Saturday: A few guns were fired this day in the direction of Lieut Kavanaugh,[14] who has received the appointment of Director of Artillery. The roar of the cannon accompanied with the Music of the Band, astonished the Indians beyond Measure, Who gazed in wonder and amazement.

November 8, 1818—Sunday: [19] The Kansas this day stole from the Sutler Several valuable articles, and a quantity of Camp equipage from the cantonment, and were retreating with their plunder when Capt Martin promptly surrounded them and made them prisoners, when they yielded up the stolen property, and were permitted to retire. In consequence of the accidental discharge of a gun, a woman[15] was this day Killed, and two Men severely wounded. The blaze of a tent which accidentially took fire was communicated to a loaded Rifle.

November 9, 1818—Monday: Five of our hunters were this day robbed by a party of Kansas, even of their coats, and a Skiff passing down the river, was fired on by them. A skiff was also stolen from the Island by the Same party. These outrageous proceedings of theirs enduced a belief that four of our hunters which had been absent several days were murdered, in consequence of which,

13 The Sacs or Sauks are an Algonquian tribe, who lived in western Illinois, southern Iowa, and northern Missouri. They were feared warriors and fought continually with most of their neighbors. Hodge, *Handbook*, II, 471–80.

14 They were not fired at Kavanaugh, but under his supervision.

15 This was probably the wife of an enlisted man. These women often worked as camp laundresses.

34

Capt Martin despatched Capt Riley, Lt Gray Qr. Mr., Doctr Gale Surgeon, and a command of sixty men, in the Genl Smith, in search of them, with orders to Capture and bring in every Kansas we should meet. Near evening they[16] were met by the hunters who had seen the Indians about six Miles ahead passing rapidly up the river, When Capt Riley dispairing of overtaking them, returned to Camp. The Indians had committed no other depredations on the hunters, than taking from them one deer.

November 10, 1818—Tuesday: Lieut Clark with Capt Magees Company, this day removed to their quarters, which are completed. Mr [Benjamin] O Fallon arrived this day from the Council Bluffs, where he had met the Ottoes and Mahas,[17] who appear friendly disposed towards the United States, And highly pleased with the proposition relative to our residence Among them. A half Breed however, who boasted of having Killed a prisoner at the Massacre at Chicago in 1812,[18] and of other heroic feats of a like nature, used every exertion to instigate the Indians there assembled to rise against the Agent. This being communicated by a chief, Mr O Fallon promptly cut off the fellows ears, gave him one hundred lashes, threw his arms[19] in the river, and set him loose. Mr O Fallon was detained ten days in assisting a trader, who had lost his boat by runing it against a planter, which broke it in two near the middle. On his [20] return, he was fired on by a party of the Kansas, about 20 Miles above this. He returned their fire from the boat, his force being insufficient to authorise a landing.

16 The use of "we" in the preceding sentence and of "they" here seems to indicate a change in authorship, but the script remains the same. Most probably a clerk is writing this from notes kept by one of the three named officers. Surgeon Gale is the only one of the three who had been with the expedition from the start and who had also accompanied the earlier detachment ahead of the main body of troops (September 16–19). Therefore, he is keeping the notes.

17 Sometimes also spelled Mahar in the journal, these are the Omaha Indians, a Siouan tribe living west of the Missouri and north of the Platte in eastern Nebraska. Hodge, *Handbook*, II, 119–21.

18 This was the attack on the evacuating column leaving Fort Dearborn on August 15, 1812. Harry L. Coles, *The War of 1812*, 58.

19 These are the Indian's weapons, not his limbs.

35

November 11, 1818—Wednesday: Mr [Benjamin] O Fallon proceeded this Morning to St Louis, in company with Captain Martin, who with a party has descended to the little River Platte in the Genl Smith, for the purpose of hunting, and recovering a public horse, which has Strayed in that direction.

November 12, 1818[20]—Thursday: Captain Riley and his Company this evening removed to their Barracks which are finished. Thus in the short space of 25 days this command have taken Timber from the forest and constructed secure and comfortable winter quarters.

Captain Martin this evening returned from his tour down the river, having descended no more than 10 miles where he met a party of the Kansas who robbed his hunters of their game, and a part of their wearing apparel. On his return he ordered the immediate seisure of the principal chief and a few Indians who fortunately happened to be present. All however escaped but the chief & two others who were put under guard in Irons to be kept as hostages for the good conduct of the tribe. Those who escaped were fired on but without effect.

November 13, 1818—Friday: Morning Rainy. One of the Indians taken into custody yesterday was this day released and dispatched to the tribe with information that unless the culprits who had committed the late depredations were delivered up the chief should continue in confinement and suffer for the agressions.

November 14, 1818—Saturday: The Command was this day put in requisition for the purpose of forming Bastions, in which to work our cannon in the two opposite angles of the Fort, and to picket in the two remaining angles.[21] Also to put up gates, thus to secure ourselves against the Indians should they be disposed to invade us. [21] Report was this evening brought in that

20 This is the first clear change of script in the manuscript.

21 These were log blockhouses built in two corners of the fort. The spaces between the barracks in the other two corners were filled with high log picket fences or stockades.

"Mouth of the Missouri River," from a lithograph by J. C. Wied

Courtesy The Missouri Historical Society

Sep' 8th Weather continues pleasant, Wind Still ahead, passed Shepherds creek on the South West side which is fifteen Miles in length, and eighty three distant up the Missouri from the Mississippi at 4 OClock arrived at Otters Island One miles in length narrow, situated high, very fertile, and is inhabited by several families from the States, On the North Side three small creeks empty themselves On the South Side, one called Ash creek, twenty yards wide, timber on the banks of the River principally cotton wood, hickory Sycamore, and Ash — encamped on the South Side opposite Otter Island, having Made fifteen Miles —

Sep' 9th Weather cloudy, Wind fair, Made Gasconade River at 11 OClock, this River falls into the Missouri from the South 100 miles from the Mississippi — is 150 Miles in length, 150 yards wide, & is twenty feet deep at its Mouth — its course is through a rough country generally Northeast, on its banks are a number of Sulphuric caves, Several American families are settled up this river — passed clear creek on the South Side, four miles above the Gasconade and two miles further Henthorns tavern, a cave on the North, passed also Rush creek in the South opposite a large Island — land on the South Side appears fertile, covered with bushes making up other timber of considerable size — on the North, land broken and rocky, Many bluffs of stupendous height front the River, Wind continuing strong and fair, Made twenty Miles this day, one Man accidentally wounded by a shot

10 Rain'd heavy last night and this Morning, in consequence of which we did not proceed until 10 OClock, When the Wind commenced blowing fair, but light, With the assistance of which and our Oars, we were able to Make good way against the current until three OClock where the Wind failed, proceeded by the aid of our cordelle until evening when we encamped on a Small Island on the South Side Made 12 Miles passed Big Muddy river, coming in from the Northeast 50 yards wide at its Mouth, and 15 Miles above the Gasconade, 3 Miles above passed little Muddy river on the same Side —

11 Left Morning rainy, No Wind passed a large creek 5 OClock on the North side, Soon after which we passed Bear creek coming in from the South, about 3 OClock Made the Ground Osage river, coming into the Missouri from the South West, through a rich level country, the Osage at its Mouth is four hundred yards wide, its junction with the Missouri is in Latitude 38°.31'.16" and 133 Miles from the Mississippi, encamped nearly opposite the Mouth of the

A sample page of the journal

the Indians were approaching us in numbers and with hostile intentions, in consequence of which our men were called from their labor to their arms, where they remained in readiness to give them a warm reception about an hour when it was discovered that the report was false.

November 15, 1818—Sunday: Night cold & frosty, morning pleasant. The Officers were this day Employed in issuing winter clothing to the troops which the advancement of the season renders requisite.

November 16, 1818—Monday: Two hunters returned last night who had been out two days during which time they had killed Six deer, which they were unable to bring in. Capt Martin thinking it dangerous from the present disturbances to trust out small parties sent Doctor Gale in the General Smith with a party of 25 men who returned with the venison & four additional deer which they killed without discovering any Indians.

November 17, 1818—Tuesday: Circumstances renders it dangerous to send out hunters unprotected in consequence of which the Commanding Officer determined to send out an Officer with a command alternately for their protection. Lieut Kavanaugh this morning went out with a party for that purpose and returned in the evening with several deer without having discovered any Indians.

A Mr Patrick[22] arrived this day with 85 Bullocks for the contractor having lost 28 on his passage through the woods. The fires with which we have several days been invested have now receded beyond our view. The Island [22] on which we are is the only spot which has escaped the ravages of the fire—consequently the only place on which we can subsist our cattle & horses.

November 18, 1818—Wednesday: Mr Rogers contractors

---

22 Robert Patrick was among the first settlers on the Miami Bottom in 1817. He owned about one thousand acres of land there and raised beef for the army. *Saline County*, 160–61.

Agent with a party of Frenchmen in his Employ returned this evening from a hunting excursion, and reported that a party of Indians of the Kansas tribe seized one of his men & robed him of his Venison & a Turkey. Also that they attempted to invest & seize his party but that they escaped by flight.

November 19, 1818—Thursday: In consequence of the discovery of Indians yesterday Capt. Martin this morning ordered out Lieut Gray with a command for the purpose of observation with orders to make prisoners of all the Indians with whom he should meet. He returned in the evening without having met with any. A few men who hunted under his protection brought in ten deer & a few Turkeys.

November 20, 1818—Friday: Lieut. Clark who went out this morning with a Command returned this evening with 10 deer but without having seen any Indians.

November 21, 1818—Saturday: The Commanding Officer this morning sent out Lieut. Field with a party of men who discovered a few lodges of the Kansas Indians and succeeded in Surprising & seizing 8 of their warriors, who on their arrival were by the order of Capt Martin immediately put under guard in Irons.

November 22, 1818—Sunday: Mr Richards[23] an interprizing trader arrived this day from Manuels Fort[24] on his return to St Louis, having disposed of his goods to a rival in the fur trade [23] who had located himself near him. He reports that the Kansas Indians have treated him very cavalierly—but that the tribes above him are well disposed.

23 There were several Richardses in St. Louis and St. Charles active in the fur trade. It is not possible to determine which Mr. Richards this is. Oglesby, *Manuel Lisa*, 170–71; John D. McDermott, "John Baptiste Richard," *The Mountain Men*, II, 289–90.

24 This is Fort Lisa, established by Manuel Lisa, a prominent St. Louis fur trader. It was on the west bank of the Missouri and two miles north of Boyer River. *DAB*, XI, 291; Oglesby, *Manuel Lisa*, 174–75. In the journal Lisa is often called Mr. Manuel.

November 23, 1818—Monday: The Indians now in confinement were this morning arraigned before Captain Martin who specified the charges exhibited against them and admitted them to plea in their own behalf.

They were charged *1st* with Theft, stealing both public and private property from the Garrison, while permitted to encamp near it. Thus repaying our hospitality and civilities with ingratitude and insult. *2d* With having robbed and plundered our hunters of their game, ammunition, and wearing apparel, thereby breaking those bonds of amity and friendship which they had pledged themselves to observe. Thus proving themselves false, treacherous, and dishonorable, unworthy either of our confidence or protection.

In reply to these charges their chief rose and after casting his eyes over the soldiers who invested him, thus addressed the Commanding Officer:

"Father—your young men are prescribed within certain bounds. Not one of them can pass that chain of sentinels without your permission. Thus ever within your power you govern them with ease. But my warriors impatient of restraint as the wild horse in the toils of the hunter, brook no controul. Free as the air which they breathe, light and impetuous as the Antelope, they bound [24] Mountains and Moor in pursuit of pleasure which nature has ordained they should enjoy. To confine them to one vally would deprive them of their subsistance; they would pine and die in penury and want.

"These woods and streams are ours; the beaver which inhabit this river and the Buffaloe which range in these forests are ours; their skins afford us clothing and shelter from the rude blasts of winter; their meat a luxurious subsistance.

"Should we then who are Lords of the Forests quit the pleasures and the adventures of the hunt, and like you, confine ourselves to one solitary valley, to practice discipline and subordination to live in idleness and indolence. No, father. In pursuit of the Elk and Antelope we will sniff the morning breeze on the mountain, and in the evening repose among the lillies of the valley revelling in the Spoils of our hunters and the embraces of our wives.[25]

"Father—these pleasures we invite you to participate, we also invest you with an equal right with ourselves, to take Meat from our forest and fish from our mountains as freely as the Great Spirit gave them to us.

"Father—We love and respect you, and Mourn that there are bad Men among us, who have done you Wrong. Their actions, Father, Were not within my controul. Punish not the innocent for the guilty. Free our hands from these chains. We will seek out the Culprits who have injured you, Altho they crouch in [25] the thickest glen, or lie concealed in the recesses of the most unaccessable Mountain.

"Father—We will deliver them to you, to punish to your Satisfaction, for the outrages they have committed against you, and pledge ourselves, that Should one of our nation at any future period envince an evil disposition towards you, We will give him to your power, that with the rod of correction, you may open his ears to reproof."

The Sophistry of this address however, did not deter the Commanding Officer from severely flagellating five of the Culprits, who were recognized as offenders. After which they were permitted to retire, Strongly enjoined to Mend their Manners and Morals.

November 24, 1818—Tuesday: A Smith Shop was this day completed, and able workmen Selected, to repair the Rifles which have been injured during our passage.

November 25, 1818—Wednesday: Captain Riley with a command descended the River three Miles this Morning, and spent the day in reconoitreing, and hunting. Captain Martin was em-

---

25 Here the writer apparently tires, because the script changes to that used by the original writer at the beginning of the next paragraph.

ployed in searching a Channel, through which to pass the boats into the Sluice on the South of the Island, but without success.

November 26, 1818—Thursday: Our hunters brought in this day 12 Deer, and report that the game is very abundant.

November 27, 1818—Friday: Mr Manuel a celebrated Indian trader, arrived from his Fort, this day. Situated about 250 Miles above this place, it consists of a few huts in which he deposits his goods, and from which he sends out his traders with outfits. He reports that the Arickaras[26] have Killed one of his Men. It appears that they were provoked to it, from the circumstance of the Ottoes, with whom this Man [26] Was trading, had killed in Action about thirty of them.

November 28, 1818—Saturday: Mr Manuel this day continued his rout to St Louis, his boat laden with 600 Buffaloe Rugs,[27] which he had procured from the Indians above.

November 29, 30, 1818—Sunday-Monday: The weather still continues pleasant. The winds during the last Month have prevailed up the River. No rain of consequence has fallen since the last of September.

December 1, 2, 1818—Tuesday-Wednesday: Cloudy with Sleet and Snow.

December 3, 1818—Thursday: A boat of the Contractor arrived this day from St Louis laden with whiskey and flour. The Captain of which reports that a little distance above Belle Fontaine, a boat Laded with flour &c for this command was sunk in consequence of runing against a Snag, which pierced her sides.

December 4, 1818—Friday: The boat which arrived yesterday was unladen, and returned this morning.

26 This warlike Caddoan tribe lived in permanent villages along the Missouri River in South Dakota. They committed repeated depredations on travelers and fur traders. Hodge, *Handbook*, I, 83–86.

27 This refers to buffalo robes or hides which the Indians wore as a sort of combination blanket and clothing. Oglesby, *Manuel Lisa*, 57, 90.

December 5, 1818—Saturday: Captain Magee formerly of the Ordnance Department, who has effected a transfer with Captain Mc Intosh of the Rifle Regiment, arrived this day from Belle Fontaine, escorted by two chiefs of the Kansas tribe, and 4 men which had enlisted on his way. Lt Field who has been out with a few men in search of the Petit River Platte, returned this evening without having discovered it.[28]

December 6, 1818—Sunday: The opperation of Amputation was performed by Doctors Gale & Clark, on William Whitney[29] a Soldier, who some time since received an accidental Rifle Shot in the Knee. The command immediately very [27] generously Subscribed Seven hundred dollars for his relief.

December 7, 1818—Monday: Wind heavy and cold from the North.

December 8, 1818—Tuesday: Wind still from the North. Colder than usual, yet clear and fair. Mr Chambers[30] an agent for the contractor, arrived this Morning from St Louis.

December 9, 1818—Wednesday: Lieut. Gray Qu Master, left this in a Skiff for Fort Osage, to relieve Capt McIntosh, lately attached to the Ordnance Department.

December 10, 1818—Thursday: Weather continues cold. Wind North. The surface of the River appears covered with floating ice, none of which Made its appearance until this Morning. The water of the River, becomes clearer as it becomes colder. Cold appears to precipitate the Wind.

---

28 Apparently the writer means that Lieutenant Field failed to reach the Little Platte. Certainly the detachment knew where the stream was, having passed it on October 13, about thirty-five miles south of Cow Island.

29 This comment indicates the writer's awareness of medical activity within the command. Private Whitney served in Captain Magee's company of the Rifle Regiment. Muster Rolls, Rifle Regiment, 1819, AGO.

30 There are at least ten men of this name in Missouri at the time. It has not been possible to identify this individual. Houck, *History of Missouri*, II, 78, 150; III, 65, 85–86, 197.

December 11, 1818—Friday: In consequence of the ice which continues floating down the River in large quantities, a boat of the contractors ascending, was compelled to unlade about 15 Miles below this place and return.

December 12, 1818—Saturday: Cloudy with a little snow, which soon disappeared.

December 13, 1818—Sunday: Capt Martin sent Capt Magee, with a party of 20 Men, in the Forsyth, to load and bring up the provisions left by the contractors boat.

December 14, 15, 1818—Monday-Tuesday: Wind from the North, with a rapid flight of snow, which continued but a few hours; which with the pressure of ice, compelled Capt Magee who had Loaded the Provisions, and ascended about a mile, to fall back, where he remained until the 15th Decembr when Capt Riley with 20 Men, was sent to his assistance.

December 16, 1818—Wednesday: Capt Magee with a part of his command returned to the cantonment. A Soldier of Capt Rileys command, who strayed, and slept out all night, returned [28] with his feet badly frozen.

December 17, 18, 1818—Thursday-Friday: Capt Riley succeeded in ascending the river as high as the lower point of Bear Medicine Island,[31] where he discovered a harbor, and left the boat with a small Guard, and returned on the 18th Decembr having crossed the river on the ice, which had stopped, and frozen solid near the boat.

December 19, 20, 21, 22, 23, 1818—Saturday-Wednesday: Weather Moderate. The Wind prevailing from the South east.

December 24, 1818—Thursday: Mr Curtis[32] and Zanona,[33]

31 Captain Riley and his detachment were about fifteen miles down river from the cantonment. They moved five miles upstream to Bear Medicine Island.
32 Cyrus Curtis was an independent fur trader who later dealt with the American Fur Company. American Fur Company Papers, MHS.
33 John B. Zenoni traded with the Osage tribe. His name is spelled variously as Zenond and Zanona. Oglesby, *Manuel Lisa,* 172, 175; Fur Trade Papers, MHS.

43

traders on the Kansas River arrived in company with 4 Osages, bringing intiligence that the Chiefs have severly punished the Indians who committed the late depridations on our hunters, and that they were pleased with punishment we had inflicted.

December 26, 27, 28, 29, 30, 1818—Friday-Wednesday: Weather clear and pleasant. Wind from the South east.

December 31, 1818—Thursday: The troops were Mustered & Inspected by Capt Martin. Their neat and Martial appearance does Much credit to their Officers.[34] An Express which Captain [John] O Fallon, had sent to the Sacks, who were hunting on the head Waters of the Kansas River, arrived with a party of Sacks richly laden with Beaver. Capt Magee finished a banquet[35] of earth and logs, raised to protect the boats from the ice, which have been drawn out of the river.

January 1, 1819—Friday: Wind from the North. Weather clear and cold. The ice which continued to float past stopped, and the river closed. Mr Partrick arrived with Cattle for the Contractor, from a little below Grand River.

January 2, 1819—Saturday: Capt [John] O Fallon commenced paying the troops to the 31st Decemr 1818. The prompt and regular Manner in which they have been paid, conduces much to reconcile them to their Secluded Situation. All who have discharged, have reenlisted.[36]

January 3, 4, 1819—Sunday-Monday: The Wind continues from the North. Weather clear and cold. River passable on the ice, opposite and below this place.

January 5, 1819—Tuesday: [29] Capt Magee an active, and

[34] Here is another indication that this account is being written by someone who is not participating in the military activity being described.

[35] A banquette is a raised earthen bank. In this case it was a dike or pier built to protect the boats. *Funk and Wagnall's Dictionary,* 222.

[36] Perhaps the men re-enlisted because they feared doing anything else. It was midwinter and difficult to get back down river. Also the Indians often robbed individuals or small groups.

enterprizing Officer, with Lieut Field and 20 Men, left this place, to ascend the Petit River Platte to its source, thence to the head-waters of the Nodaway[37] which they intend to follow to its junction with the Missouri, on a tour of discovery. An Express arrived from Franklin which had been sent by Capt [John] O Fallon bringing the President's Message &c.[38]

January 6, 7, 8, 9, 10, 1819—Wednesday-Sunday: Weather moderate. Wind from the South, and east. The ice on the river appears to decay rapidly, river impassible on the ice.

January 11, 1819—Monday: Weather more Moderate. Wind still from the south, and river entirely clear of ice. In consequence of which Lieut Clark with a command of 20 Men in company of Doctor Clarke is sent to bring up the Forsyth, which is still laden with provisions at Bear Medicine Island.

January 12, 1819—Tuesday: Weather moderate and Clear. Wind North. Some appearance of floating ice. Lieut Clark Succeeded in bringing the boat safe to Camp.

January 13, 1819—Wednesday: Weather Moderate. Wind from the North. Some appearance of ice floating. It appears that the return boat of the contractors, grounded in a Sluice 30 miles below, and that the crew have deserted. Mr Chambers sent this morning two men to Guard it.

January 14, 1819—Thursday: A Soldier in a passion stabbed a Negro of Mr Pactrick. The Knife entered the lungs a little below the left Breast. The wound is not mortal.[39]

An Express arrived with dispatches from Col Chambers with intiligence that Steam Boats are building to transport the 2nd Battalion up the Missouri, early in the Spring.[40]

[37] The Nodaway River enters the Missouri in Andrew County, Missouri, about twenty miles northwest of St. Joseph.

[38] This was President James Monroe's Annual Message to Congress, November 17, 1818. 15 Cong., 2 sess., *Senate Document No. 1*, 10.

[39] Here is still another medical judgment by the author.

[40] This refers to the steamboats, *Expedition, Johnson, Jefferson,* and *Calhoun,*

January 15, 1819—Friday: Capt [John] O Fallon left this for St Louis, attended by a discharged Soldier, and Several Men in his employ.

January 16, 1819—Saturday: Weather Moderate. Wind from the South east. Capt Martin sent an express to over take and accompany Capt [John] O Fallon with dispatches.

January 17, 18, 19, 20, 1819—Sunday-Wednesday: Wind from the South East. Weather Moderate, the river perfectly clear of ice.

January 21, 1819—Thursday: [30] One of the Soldiers who accompanied Capt [John] O Fallon to Fort Osage, returned. It appears that he lost one of his horses, which fell into a quagmire, from which he could not extricate it, and was compelled to Shoot it.

January 22, 23, 24, 25, 1819—Friday-Monday: Wind from the South and East. Weather warm and pleasant.

January 26, 1819—Tuesday: Mr Chambers one of the contractors Agents, left this for Franklin.

January 27, 1819—Wednesday: Mr Julian[41] of the Indian dept arrived from Fort Lisa. He was attacked in the night, at the Mouth of the River Platte, by he believes a party of the Sacks who killed two Indians that attended him, and retired, leaving behind a new Rifle which appeared to be British Manufacture.[42]

which the contractor James Johnson tried to use on the Missouri during the summer of 1819. William D. Hubbell, "The First Steamboats on the Missouri" (ed. by Vivian K. McLarty), *Missouri Historical Review*, Vol. LI (July, 1957), 375; Wesley, "A Still Larger View," *NDHQ*, Vol. V (July, 1931), 224; Nichols, *General Atkinson*, 57–59.

41 This is Stephen Julian. Occasionally his name is spelled Julien. He served as an interpreter in 1819. Thwaites, *James Account*, I, 58, 192, 210–11; John R. Bell, *The Journal of Captain John R. Bell* . . . (ed. by Harlan M. Fuller and LeRoy R. Hafen), 103–104 (hereafter Fuller and Hafen, *Bell Journal*).

42 Probably a light fusil or fur-trade gun. It was not unusual for the Indians to get such weapons in Canada or from British traders. One goal of this expedition was to reduce this British influence and trade, but as late as 1832, the Sac and Fox Indians who fought in the Blackhawk War were still known as the "British Band." William T. Hagan, *The Sac and Fox Indians*, 141–47.

January 28, 29, 30, 1819—Thursday-Saturday: Wind still from the South & east. Weather warm and pleasant.

January 31, 1819—Sunday: Mr Julian, Mr Patrick, and Mr Bodwoin[43] left this for St Louis. The avowed intention of the latter who has been pilot of Capt [John] O Fallons boat, is to prosecute a Court Martial, which tried and punished him, for running his boat against a public boat, in ascending the River, which did it much injury.

February 1, 2, 3, 1819—Monday-Wednesday: Weather Pleasant. Wind from the South. Numerous Geese, Swans, ducks and other birds of passage, have made their appearance, Winging their flight to the North. A few have been Killed.

February 4, 1819—Thursday: Capt Magee, and Lieut Field with their Command, who have been on a tour to the Little River Platte, returned. They pursued a Northeast course, from this place, to the Platte, which they Made at a distance of forty Miles. At the point at which they struck, it appeared 80 yards wide, but [31] very shallow. A short distance above, it deminished in Size and forked, each branch about 20 yards wide. After pursuing it about eighty Miles, they left it, and Made the Missouri 30 Miles above this place, at a distance of six Miles.[44] The land between the Platte and Missouri, is rich, and covered with Majestic Forest timber, interspersed with Several small water courses. The Command Killed but eighty deer, and 180 Turkeys, not caring to kill more than they could consume.

February 5, 6, 1819—Friday-Saturday: Wind Southeast. Rain which commenced on the night of the 4th continuing. The only rain of consequence, which has fallen since the 1st Septem 1818.

---

43 This was Louis or Louison Beaudoin. His name is also spelled Baudoin and Boudouin. He commanded a Missouri River barge for Manuel Lisa in 1807, and another for John O'Fallon in 1818–19. Oglesby, *Manuel Lisa*, 35; Manuscript Index, MHS.

44 The detachment traveled only six miles from the Little Platte to reach the Missouri, doing so about thirty miles above the cantonment.

February 7, 1819—Sunday: Weather pleasant. Wind from the South. Our hunters are Still successful, Usually bringing into Camp from ten to fifteen deer and as Many Turkeys of a day.

February 8, 1819—Monday: Mr Rogers Contractors agent left this place with a Command of twenty Men for Fort Osage, to bring up the provisions in Store at that place.

February 9, 1819—Tuesday: Captain Martin commenced repairing the boats for a remove up the River, which the beauty of the Season Seems to invite.

February 10, 1819—Wednesday: The troops commenced drill, which owing to the excessive fatigue duty[45] had been previously omitted.

February 11, 1819—Thursday: Doctors Gale & Clark Made a tour to the old Kansas Village, for the purpose of examining a bed of Yellow Ochre[46] in its Neighborhood, the Soil [32] Cliffs, &c. The Prairies and woods, appeared animated with deer, and turkeys.

February 12, 13, 1819—Friday-Saturday: Wind still from the South and east. Weather pleasant.

February 14, 1819—Sunday: Capt Martin, Capt Magee & Doct Gale, With a command of Twenty Men, in the Genl. Smith, ascended the river for the purpose of hunting.[47]

February 15, 1819—Monday: Wind from the North. Weather cold.

February 16, 1819—Tuesday: Wind from the North & East accompanied with a rapid flight of snow.

---

45 This refers to work details such as propelling the boats, erecting the buildings, and hunting.

46 Yellow ochre is a native earth consisting of iron peroxid, water, and clay. It is used for pigment and for paint. *Funk and Wagnall's Dictionary*, 1707.

47 Here Dr. Gale leaves the camp. The entries for the days he is absent are minimal, but those following his return include more detail.

February 17, 1819—Wednesday: Wind from the North West. Weather clear and cold. Some appearance of floating ice, occasioned by the freezing of the Snow, which had fallen into the Water yesterday.

February 18, 19, 1819—Thursday-Friday: Wind from the North. Weather cold. The ice continues to run in the river, but in less quantities.

February 20, 21, 1819—Saturday-Sunday: Weather More Moderate. Wind from the east. The river is clear of ice, and the Snow has disappeared.

February 22, 1819—Monday: The birth day of the illustrious, Washington was ushered in with a national Salute from our artillery. The day was celebrated at Capt Rileys quarters who prepared an excellent dinner on the occasion.

February 23, 1819—Tuesday: Weather Moderate. Wind from the West.

February 24, 1819—Wednesday: Capt Martin, Capt Magee, & Doct Gale with the command, returned from their hunting excursion, having taken fifty deer, sixty turkeys, a bear three cubs, and a quantity of honey. The bear was Killed by [Private] Moses Mc Clanahan of Capt Magees company, who evinced a degree of courage seldom equalled. [33] A buck which he had Killed, proved so burthensome as induced him to leave it, and return to the camp for assistance. A man was accordingly despatched to assist him in bringing it in. On his arrival at the Spot, where he had left it, he discovered a part of it had been consumed by some wild beast. While endeavouring to trace its retreat, he was surprised to hear a noise issue from a hole in an adjacent large Sycamore tree which on climbing, he found was occasioned by a bear and three cubs. He had no sooner discovered the head of the bear, which had ascended near the hole, to view her invader, than he cut a grape vine pending from a limb near him, to the lower

49

[end] of which, his companion, attached a loaded gun, Which Mc Clanahan drew up and discharged at the head of the bear. The ball passed through her nose. He then lowered his grape vine, and received a second loaded Gun, with which he dispatched her. Mr Rogers returned from Osage, with a boat loaded with Flour, beef & whiskey.

February 25, 26, 1819—Thursday-Friday: Weather pleasant. Wind from the South & east. Mr Kennerly[48] and Mr Richards who arrived here on the 23rd from St Louis, proceed this day 26th to Fort Lisa, for the purpose [of] taking possession of the Indian goods, belonging to the fur company, in possession of Mr Manuel, who has been expelled from the company.[49]

February 27, 28, 1819—Saturday-Sunday: Weather pleasant. Wind still from the South & east. The troops were this day, 28th Mustered, and Inspected by Capt Martin. They were much improved in appearance.

March 1, 1819—Monday: Weather cold. Wind from the North West with snow.

March 2, 1819—Tuesday: [34] Wind from the North east, Weather Chilly. The ground is covered with Snow yet there is no appearance of ice in the river. Lieut Clark Lt Kavanaugh, Doct Gale & Mr Rogers, with a command of twenty Men, in the Genl. Smith, ascended the river about 35 miles for the purpose of hunting.

March 3, 1819—Wednesday: Wind from the Southeast. Weather Moderate.

48 This seems to be George H. Kennerly, a St. Louis businessman, who had resigned his army commission less than two months earlier. It is unusual that he is not referred to by his military title of captain. Gale, a New Englander, would be less likely to use military titles for civilians than would Kavanaugh, a Kentuckian. Oglesby, *Manuel Lisa,* 170; Heitman, *Historical Register,* I, 592; Stella M. Drumm (comp.), "The Kennerlys of Virginia," *Missouri Historical Society Collections,* Vol. VI (Oct., 1928), 108-109.

49 Lisa and his partners could not agree on policy or on finances. Oglesby, *Manuel Lisa,* 169-71.

March 4, 1819—Thursday: Wind Still from the South east. The Snow which fell on the 1st has disappeared.

March 5, 6, 7, 8, 1819—Friday-Monday: Wind still from the South & east. Weather Cloudy & Chilly.

March 9, 10, 1819—Tuesday-Wednesday: The boats are Launched, having been calked and patched.

March 11, 1819—Thursday: Lieut Clark, Lt Kavanaugh, Doct Gale & Mr Rogers, with the command, returned in the Genl Smith, from their hunting excursion with many deer, Racoons, turkeys, & some honey. Capt Rileys Men have Succeded lately in Killing several bear.

March 12, 1819—Friday: Wind from the North. Weather Cloudy.

March 13, 1819—Saturday: Capt Riley, & Dr Clark, with a few men in the General Smith, ascended the river, for the purpose of hunting & fishing in Goslin lake 8 Miles above.[50] Lieut Field also with a small party of Men, went down the river to the old Kansas Village on a hunting excursion.

March 14, 15, 1819—Sunday-Monday: Wind from the North West. Weather Cloudy and Cold, with Snow.

March 16, 17, 1819[51]—Tuesday-Wednesday: Cloudy and cold. Some Ice floating on the River.

March 18, 1819—Thursday: Fair and warm. Wind south. The Snow which fell on the 15th has disappeared. Captain Riley & Dr Clarke returned from hunting.

March 19, 1819—Friday: [35] Wind South. Fair and warm. Lieut Field returned from his hunting excursion.

[50] An oxbow lake was in the vicinity of Sugar Lake in Platte County, Missouri.
[51] Here the script changes, and a third writer kept the next portion of the journal.

March 20, 1819—Saturday: Wind North. Weather fair but cold. River clear of Ice.

March 21, 22, 1819—Sunday-Monday: Wind Northern. Fair but cold.

March 23, 24, 25, 1819—Tuesday-Thursday: Wind Southeast. Fair and warm.

March 26, 27, 28, 29, 1819—Friday-Monday: Wind Southeast. Showers with thunder and lightening. Mr Andrew Woods[52] from St Louis arrived on the 26th, on his way to Mr Manuel Lisa's establishment at Council Bluffs.

March 30, 31, 1819—Tuesday-Wednesday: Wind South. Fair and warm. A Diary of the weather will in future be kept in a book distinct with meterological observations.[53]

April 1, 1819—Thursday: Mr Rogers Contractors agent sent a return boat to St Louis.

April 2, 3, 1819—Friday-Saturday: The officers are employed in drilling with blank cartridges in the woods. One party fantastically paint themselves to represent Indians while the other party personate Riflemen and act by bugle signals alternately acting on the offensive and defensive as occasion may require. Judges are appointed to decide the merits of the sham combatants, A species of drill excites much emulation and promises to conduce much to the perfection of the Battalion. A Soldier of Captain Rileys Company received an accidental shot in the thigh which will disable him a short time only.

April 4, 1819—Sunday: Lieut Clark Dr Clarke and Mr Giroll[54]

52 Mr. Woods was a member of the Missouri Fur Company. Oglesby, *Manuel Lisa*, 172; Chittenden, *The American Fur Trade*, I, 147.

53 This further substantiates Gale's authorship of the journal. As regimental surgeon it was his duty to keep and report weather information. These records were kept and submitted quarterly beginning on January 1, 1819. Percy M. Ashburn, *A History of the Medical Department of the United States Army*, 90; Thomas Lawson, *Statistical Report on the Sickness and Mortality of the Army . . . ,* 12–15.

General Henry Atkinson   Captain John O'Fallon

Major Benjamin O'Fallon   Manuel Lisa

left this in a canoe to meet Mr Barthold[55] one of the Fur Company on his way up the River to Council Bluffs.

April 5, 1819—Monday: Capt Martin with a crew in the General Smith left this on an excursion up the River for the purpose of procuring game and honey.

April 6, 1819—Tuesday: The Cotton[wood] Trees have budded and the Grass in the meadows exposed to the Sun is two inches high.

April 7, 1819—Wednesday: Lieut Clark and party returned in company with Mr Barthold who has two Mackinaw boats[56] principally laden with goods for Capt [36] [John] O Fallon, who having unladen they proceeded to Fort Lisa. Dr Gale accompanied him to join Capt Martin 30 miles above.

April 8, 9, 10, 11, 12, 1819—Thursday-Monday: Troops constantly drilling. They have made such improvement as does honor to the gentlemen who command them.

April 13, 1819—Tuesday: Lieut Colonel Morgan[57] & Quarter Master Palmer[58] arrived, the former from St. Louis the latter from Fort Osage.

April 14, 1819—Wednesday: Lieut Colonel [Morgan] assumes the command of this post. Capt Martin and Dr Gale arrived from their hunting excursion having taken two young bears a large quantity of honey and killed a panther with a variety of other game.

---

54 Giroll was an agent for Sutler John O'Fallon. Other than that he is not identifiable.

55 Bartholomew Berthold was a St. Louis merchant and fur trader. Conrad, *Encyclopedia of Missouri*, I, 212; Oglesby, *Manuel Lisa*, 168, 170–71.

56 A flat-bottomed boat with a pointed bow and square stern, this shallow-draft boat was propelled with oars and was used for river travel with heavy cargoes.

57 Lieutenant Colonel Willoughby Morgan was second in command of the Rifle Regiment. Heitman, *Historical Register*, I, 726.

58 First Lieutenant Loring Palmer was the quartermaster officer of the Rifle Regiment. *Ibid.*, I, 767.

April 15, 1819—Thursday: Lieut Field was dispatched in the General Smith with a crew of 25 men to Manuel Lisa's Establishment to take charge of the public goods at that place consisting of presents for the Indians with orders to remain untill the Battalion shall arrive. The contractor having failed, Captain Magee with his company proceeded by order up the River to subsist his men by hunting.

April 16, 17, 1819—Friday-Saturday: Captain[59] received orders to proceed with his company down the River for the purpose of subsisting his men on wild meat but did not go untill the 17th in consequence of high winds.

April 18, 19, 1819—Sunday-Monday: River rose two feet perpendicular. Quarter Master [Palmer] left the 18th for Franklin to purchase provisions.

April 20, 1819—Tuesday: A messenger arrived from Captain Magee and Lieut Field who informed us that they were lying seven miles above wind bound[60] and that the latter had accidentally broke the mast of his Boat by running under a tree which projected over the river.

April 21, 1819—Wednesday: Captain Rileys hunters brought in two bears. His company remains in camp and is subsisted by sending out hunters who kill game while [37] others pack it to the cantonment.

April 22, 1819—Thursday: A soldier of Captain Magees command who had been injured by the falling of a tree arrived and informed us that Captain Magee and Lieut Field were lying at Independence Creek[61] windbound 22 miles above this place.

---

59 This is Captain Martin, because Captain Magee's company went north of the camp on April 15, and Captain Riley's men remained at Cow Island (see April 23 entry).

60 This means that contrary wind had prevented their sailing.

61 This enters the Missouri about fifteen miles north of Cow Island and three miles north of Atchison, Kansas.

April 23, 24, 25, 26, 27, 1819—Friday-Tuesday: The camp appears deserted. Captain Martins & Captain Magees company continue hunting, the one above the other below this place. Many of Capt Rileys are also hunting subsistance.

April 28, 1819—Wednesday: Captain Magees company arrived with ten days subsistence consisting of dried venison. Lieut Palmer Quarter Master also arrived from below. He reports that he was attacked below the Kansas river by a party of Ottoes and Ioway[62] Indians who pursued him in a canoe from the shore where a large number were assembled. That to avoid them he ran his canoe on the opposite shore and with two men who accompanied him fled to the woods. One of his men however was captured from [whom] they took fifty dollars in silver and his wearing apparrel &c. He was detained untill evening bound and after robbing the canoe of every thing they loosed him and let him go. Same day he arrived at Fort Osage with the canoe. Lieut Palmer arrived by land the same day, and immediately proceeded to Grand River and dispatched Mr Patrick with a drove of cattle for the command.

April 29, 1819—Thursday: Captain Martins Company arrived from below with a large quantity of dried meat. One of his men has been killed by an accidental shot.

April 30, 1819—Friday: Troops were mustered and inspected [by] Lieut Colonel Morgan.

May 1, 1819—Saturday: Mr Patrick who we learn passed Fort Osage with Cattle ten days since has not yet appeared from which circumstance it is presumed that the Indians who robbed Lieut Palmer have fallen in with him. In consequence of which Captain Riley received orders to select [38] seventy men and proceed by water to Blue Water River[63] below the Kansas and take

---

[62] The Iowas were a Siouan tribe. They lived along the Little Platte, Chariton, Grand, and Missouri rivers. Hodge, *Handbook*, I, 612–14.

[63] This stream joins the Missouri a few miles south of the Kansas River (see October 12, 1818, entry).

prisoners or drive away the Indians who committed the late outrages, should they remain lurking near the River.

May 2, 1819—Sunday: Captain Riley Lieut Kavanaugh Dr Gale and Mr Giroll with a command proceeded down the river in the Forsyth and arrived at the mouth of the little Platte without having discovered any signs of Indians.[64]

May 3, 1819—Monday: Captain Riley with the command fell down the Blue a little above the mouth of which a canoe in which the Indian party had crossed to the left Bank of the Missouri was discovered. Scouts were sent immediately on their trail but returned without them. Their trail appeared two days old runing Northwest. Lieut Kavanaugh proceeded with a party to Fort Osage by land in search of Mr Patrick.[65] Soon after which Captain Magee arrived in a canoe with the intelligence that Mr Patrick arrived at Martin Cantonment on the 2nd with the principle part of his cattle. His delay was caused by his having fallen in with the Indians who opposed his proceeding, shot several of his cattle and forced them back to Fort Osage from the Kansas River to which place he followed them.

May 4, 1819—Tuesday: Captain Riley arrived on his return to Camp at Kansas River where was a party of Osage Indians in pursuit of the Ioways and Ottoes who had also stolen from them a number of horses. They were supplied with ammunition assisted across the Missouri and encouraged to avenge us as well as themselves. They will probably overtake and surprise the hostile party.

May 5, 1819—Wednesday: [39] Mr Manuel Lisa on his way to his establishment in a boat laden with goods overtook Captain Rileys Command at Kansas River to whose politeness we were indebted for a quantity of pickled oysters & spanish segars. A Boat

[64] Here the narrative follows this detachment. Therefore, the author is one of these officers.
[65] Lieutenant Kavanaugh leaves the others, but the journal is kept by someone remaining with Captain Riley's detachment. Gale is the only officer except Riley left.

56

of Mr Patricks laden with whiskey for Martin Cantonment also overtook us at this place.[66]

May 6, 1819—Thursday: Captain Riley proceeded gradually up the River and arrived at the Cantonment on the 12th. The Troops were classed and commenced shooting at targets with ball cartridges at which they continued untill the 22nd daily practicing. Those who hit a circul of three inches diameter off hand fifty yards three times in six were raised from the awkward squad to the 2nd class. Those who can hit the same mark one hundred yards three times in six are raised to the first Class. They make rapid improvement. There are but few who are not in the first class.

May 23, 1819—Sunday: Lieut Clark Lieut Palmer Dr Gale and Mr Potts with a party went to Goslin Lake ten miles above this on a hunting excursion and returned the twenty fifth with a Bear some racoons deer geese cat and buffaloe fish and several soft shelled turtles.

May 26, 27, 28, 29, 30, 31, 1819—Wednesday-Monday: Troops employed at Drill. Captain Riley's hunters brought in several bears. Turkeys lean and unfit for use.

June 1, 2, 3, 4, 5, 6, 7, 8, 1819—Tuesday-Tuesday: Small boats have passed down the river from Manuel's fort loaded with furs. Among them Mr Barthold's with whom Whitney an invalid soldier who has lost a leg took passage. The Troops are now destitute of Flour. The last having been issued four days since.

June 9, 1819—Wednesday: A Boat from Chariton arrived with whiskey from the Contractor.

June 14, 1819—Monday: Lieut Clark, Lieut Kavanaugh and Dr Gale with their party of men returned from a hunting excursion. An express [40] also arrived from Fort Osage which brings

---

[66] The use of "we" in the first sentence of this entry and "us" in the second shows that the writer is with Captain Riley's detachment.

intelligence that a Steam Boat has succeeded in ascending as high as Franklin.[67] That the Troops destined for this expedition are at Belle Fontaine.[68] Also that Steam Boats have arrived for their transportation.

June 15, 1819—Tuesday: Lieut Clarke who is in arrest on a charge of having maltreated a Citizen proceeded to Fort Osage for evidence.

June 22, 1819—Tuesday: Mr Manuel Lisa passed this from his fort at Council Bluffs with two boats laden with furs. He informs us that Lieut Field had taken five of the Ottoes and Iowa Indians who robbed Lieut Palmer and severely punished them for their audacity. Lieut Field remains in possession of Manuel Lisa's establishment.

June 24, 1819—Thursday: Lieut Clark returned from Fort Osage with intelligence that the 6th Regiment of Infantry has arrived at Belle Fontaine under the command of Colonel Atkinson[69] who with the Riflemen under the command of Colonel Chambers are shortely to embark on the Missouri Expedition.

June 30, 1819—Wednesday: The battalion was inspected by Lieut Colonel Morgan who complimented them on their martial appearance.

July 6, 1819—Tuesday: Contractor failed which compelled Col Morgan to send Captain Martin with his company up and Capt Magee with his down the River to seek subsistence. Lieut

67 This was the *Independence*, which reached Franklin on May 28, 1819. Hubbell, "First Steamboats on the Missouri," 375; Houck, *History of Missouri*, III, 198; *Howard and Cooper Counties*, 122–24.

68 The Sixth Infantry Regiment arrived in St. Louis on June 7, 1819, and then moved to Bellefontaine. Henry Atkinson to John Calhoun, June 7, 1819, Secretary of War, Letters Received, Record Group 107, National Archives.

69 Colonel Henry Atkinson commanded the Sixth Infantry Regiment, the Ninth Military Department, and the Missouri Expedition. He remained as the highest ranking army officer in the West until his death in 1842. Nichols, *General Atkinson*, 50–55, 58.

Clark and Dr Gale accompanied Captain Magee.[70] Mr Rogers Contractors agent left this for the interior.

July 14, 1819—Wednesday: Capt Magee arrived at Fort Osage and found the Contractor had failed there also. The sand bars are covered with water which prevents the deer from frequenting them and the under growth in the forest is so luxuriant as to effectually secure them from the view of the hunters. Thus our subsistence is precarious. Our men ever ingenious in extremity however practice a decoy [41] which operates on the Maternal feelings of the females which at this season have their young by imitating with an artificial bleat the cries of the fawn in distress.[71] At sound of which the doe regardless of her own safety rushes to the spot in the utmost consternation and is shot down. Nothing but necessity can justify this barbarous practice.

July 21, 1819—Wednesday: Colonel Chambers arrived at Fort Osage with the second battalion of the Rifle Regiment in four boats accompanied by a boat of the Contractors.[72] He also is nearly destitute of provisions and remaining there for a supply. Colo. Atkinson with the 6th Infantry are on their way up the River in Steam Boats.[73]

July 22, 1819—Thursday: Captain Magee proceeded up the River from Fort Osage leisurely stopping to hunt at the most desirable points. His boat swung near Diamond Island upon a Drift and was narrowly saved with the loss of mast sail and rigging.

70 Here Dr. Gale leaves the cantonment, and once more the narrative follows the detachment he accompanies.

71 The use of "our" in the preceding two sentences indicates that the writer is with Captain Magee's detachment.

72 These troops left Bellefontaine on June 14, 1819. *St. Louis Enquirer*, June 16, 1819.

73 The Sixth Infantry left St. Louis on July 4 and 5 on board the steamboats *Johnson, Jefferson,* and *Expedition* and on four keelboats. The steamers immediately ran aground, so Atkinson sent the keels on ahead up the river. John O'Fallon to Thomas A. Smith, July 7, 1819, Smith Papers, State Historical Society of Missouri.

August 1, 1819—Sunday: 150 of the Kansa Indians arrived at Martin Cantonment for the purpose of meeting Major [Benjamin] O Fallon Indian agent who is daily expected.[74]

August 2, 1819—Monday: Lieut Clark & Palmer arrived from Fort Osage & Lieut Kavanaugh joined Captain Magee at Diamond Island.

August 4, 1819—Wednesday: A boat laden with flour and bacon arrived from Franklin.

August 10, 1819—Tuesday: Captain Magee came up within ten miles of the cantonment and Dr Gale & Lieut Kavanaugh returned to it.

August 11, 1819—Wednesday: Captain Martin arrived from his hunting excursion.[75] He has been very successful having killed 300 deer 20 bears and collected five barrels of honey. A second man of his has been killed by an accidental shot. The Indians fatigued with waiting for Major [Benjamin] O Fallon returned to their village.

August 12, 1819—Thursday: Dr Clarke who has resigned and Mr Giroll Sutlers agent left this place for Philadelphia.

August 13, 1819—Friday: [42] Captain Riley left this place for Fort Osage.

August 14, 1819—Saturday: Two men from Franklin arrived at the Cantonment with 70 head of Cattle and report that a keel boat of the Infantry Commanded by Captain Livingston[76] stove near Grand River and sunk at the expense of all her lading which was lost and a woman and child were drowned.

August 15, 1819—Sunday: Steam Boat Western Engineer com-

---

74 The August 1 through August 10 entries seem to have been written from notes kept by two individuals, one with Captain Magee and the other at Martin Cantonment.

75 This is Captain Martin returning from the north, not Magee from the south.

76 Captain John P. Livingston, Sixth Infantry. Heitman, *Historical Register*, I, 636.

manded by Major Long of the Engineers [77] on a voyage of discovery arrived in five and half days from Fort Osage. On her approach a salute was fired which was returned from the garrison. The Officers of the Cantonment hailed the arrival of Major Long with the highest gratification for whom they had formed a warm attachment during his tour up the Mississippi, not more on account of his professional attainments and enterprise than his suavity of manner and amiabliness of disposition.

August 16, 1819—Monday: Lieut Field arrived from the Council Bluffs destitute of subsistence. Two boats also arrived from St Louis belonging to Captain [John] O Fallon Suttler.

August 17, 1819—Tuesday: A boat arrived laden with flour for sale which Colonel Morgan purchased for the use of the Troops. Captain Bissell[78] agent for Capt [John] O Fallon who arrived on the 16th in charge of the Suttlers boats dispatched one of them laden with goods up to the Council Bluffs to await the arrival [of] the troops. The Officers gave Major Long and Major [Benjamin] O Fallon a dinner distinguished not so much by variety of viands and delicious wines as for the good humor which prevailed.

August 19, 1819—Thursday: A boat belonging to Capt. [John] O Fallon and a boat laden with public provisions passed for Council Bluffs.

August 23, 1819—Monday: Two hundred Kansa Indians arrived with whom Major [Benjamin] O Fallon counciled on the

[77] Stephen H. Long commanded the so-called Scientific Expedition in 1819–20. His steamboat, the *Western Engineer,* was specially built so that it could operate on the shallow western rivers. In order to impress the Indians, the boat looked as though it were riding on the back of a serpent. All of the machinery was hidden and the steam and smoke escaped from the mouth of a serpent-like head at the bow. Jessie Poesch, *Titian Ramsay Peale 1799–1885* . . . , 25; Wood, *Stephen H. Long,* 62–64; Heitman, *Historical Register,* I, 640.

[78] Lewis Bissell was a St. Louis businessman and a former army officer. Conrad, *Encyclopedia of Missouri,* I, 279; Heitman, *Historical Register,* I, 221.

24th.[79] Gave them a few presents and such directions as should guide their conduct.

August 25, 1819—Wednesday: [43] Major Long left this in the Steam Boat Western Engineer for the Council Bluffs accompanied by Lieut Field in the General Smith. Major [Benjamin] O Fallon Indian Agent and Lieut Graham[80] of the Artillery are of Major Longs party.

August 28, 1819—Saturday: A small trading boat passed up the River.

August 29, 1819—Sunday: Major Biddle[81] of the Artillery Dr Say[82] and Dr Jessup[83] Naturalists Mr Seymour[84] and Mr Peale[85] animal and landscape painters Mr Swift[86] a Cadet and Mr Dougherty[87] Indian Interpreter all of Major Longs party arrived from the Kansa Village. They were proceeding leisurely by land

79 According to the Long journals, Major O'Fallon met with about 175 Kansas and Osage Indians. The agent denounced the Indians for their depredations. Thwaites, *James Account*, I, 176–78; Wood, *Stephen H. Long*, 82.

80 Second Lieutenant James D. Graham, Corps of Artillery. Heitman, *Historical Register*, I, 468.

81 Captain (brevet major) Thomas Biddle, Jr., Corps of Artillery. *Ibid.*, I, 217; Wood, *Stephen H. Long*, 74.

82 Dr. Thomas Say was a prominent entomologist. He participated in at least three government expeditions between 1817 and 1823. *DAB*, XIV, 401–402; Fuller and Hafen, *Bell Journal*, 87.

83 Augustus E. Jessup was the geologist for the expedition. Thwaites, *James Account*, I, 41–42; Wood, *Stephen H. Long*, 69.

84 Samuel Seymour was a prominent painter and artist. He was the first artist to portray the Rocky Mountains, but most of his sketches were lost or destroyed. John F. McDermott, "Samuel Seymour: Pioneer Artist of the Plains and Rockies," *Smithsonian Report for 1950*, 497–509.

85 Titian R. Peale was a member of the famous Philadelphia Peale family of artists and naturalists. He accompanied Major Long as an assistant naturalist. Poesch, *Titian R. Peale*, 23–24.

86 William H. Swift was a cadet at West Point when assigned to accompany Long. After serving as an army engineer for thirty-six years, he resigned to become president of several northeastern railroads. Heitman, *Historical Register*, I, 941; *DAB*, XVIII, 249–50.

87 John Dougherty served as an employee of the Missouri Fur Company in 1809–10 in the Rocky Mountains. He spent six years trapping along the Columbia River before joining the Long party as an interpreter. Conrad, *Encyclopedia of Missouri*, II, 305–307; Oglesby, *Manuel Lisa*, 83, 94.

to the Council Bluffs for the purpose of making researches into the arena of Nature—when they were made prisoners six miles from the Kansa village by a war party of the pawnees who took away their horses and plundered them of their travelling equipage which compelled [them] to retrograde to this place. The Steam Boat Expedition laden with provisions with a part of the 6th Infantry on Board arrived. Their approach was announced by the roar of artillery which was answered from the Cantonment. Two keel boats laden with provisions also arrived.

August 30, 1819—Monday: Colonel Chambers with the 2nd Battalion of Riflemen and a part of the 6th Infantry arrived in keels. This long wished for union was hailed with reiterated Cheers and the roar of artillery from the shore and from the Flotilla.

August 31, 1819—Tuesday: Major Biddle acting Inspector Genl Mustered and Inspected the Troops both Infantry and Riflemen. Colo. Atkinson and Capt [John] O Fallon Sutler arrived from St Louis.

September 3, 1819—Friday: Col. Chambers assumed the command of Martin Cantonment and complimented the 1st Battalion on its martial appearance.

September 4, 1819—Saturday: A Court Martial sat on the trial of Lieut Clark which acquitted him of the charge of having maltreated a citizen.

PART III

Cow Island to Council Bluffs
1819

September 5, 1819—Sunday: [44] The Expedition under the Command of Col. Atkinson resumed its tour up the Missouri in keels as follows:

1st the Riflemen Commanded by Col. Chambers

1st Boat
Colo. Chambers
Capt. Martin
Lieut Pentland Adjt[1]
Lieut Mc Crea[2]

2nd Boat
Captain Riley
Lieut Palmer Quart. Mast.

3rd Boat
Lieut Kavanaugh

4th Boat
Capt Magee
Lieut Shannon[3]
Dr Malone[4] Surg Mate
Dr Jessup Naturalist

5th Boat
Lieut Colo. Morgan
Capt. Gray
Dr Gale Surgeon
Dr Say Naturalist

6th Boat
Lieut Keith[5]

7th Boat
Col Atkinson
Major Biddle Insp. Genl.

---

1 First Lieutenant Charles Pentland, Rifle Regiment adjutant. Heitman, *Historical Register*, I, 783.

2 Second Lieutenant William D. McCray, Rifle Regiment. *Ibid.*, I, 661.

3 Second Lieutenant Samuel Shannon, Rifle Regiment. *Ibid.*, I, 877.

4 Surgeon Perry D. Meloan, Rifle Regiment. *Ibid.*, I, 702.

5 Second Lieutenant Daniel Keith, Rifle Regiment. *Ibid.*, I, 588.

Capt. Smith A. A. A. G.[6]
Lieut Scott[7]

2nd The 6th Infantry Command by Major Humphreys[8]

8th Boat	12th Boat
Major Humphreys	Capt Boardman[9]
Lieut Staniford Adjt[10]	Capt Livingston
Lieut Givens[11]	
9th Boat	13th Boat
Major Ketchum[12]	Major Foster[13]
	Lieut Durand[14]
	Dr Nichol[15] Surg. Mate
10th Boat	14th Boat—Sutler's
Captain Reed[16]	Capt Bissell
Lieut Allison[17]	Mr Potts
	Mr Rannie[18]
11th Boat	15th Boat
Capt. Hamilton[19]	Provisions Boat
Lieut Mansfield[20]	
	16th Boat
	Provisions Boat

[6] Captain Thomas Floyd Smith, acting assistant adjutant general, Sixth Infantry. *Ibid.*, I, 903.

[7] Second Lieutenant Martin Scott, Rifle Regiment. *Ibid.*, I, 869.

[8] Major Gad Humphreys, Sixth Infantry. *Ibid.*, I, 555.

[9] Captain Elijah Boardman, Sixth Infantry. *Ibid.*, I, 227.

[10] First Lieutenant Thomas Staniford, regimental adjutant, Sixth Infantry. *Ibid.*, I, 915.

[11] Second Lieutenant William G. Givens, Sixth Infantry. *Ibid.*, I, 459.

[12] Captain (brevet major) Daniel Ketchum, Sixth Infantry. *Ibid.*, I, 595.

[13] Captain (brevet major) William S. Foster, Sixth Infantry. *Ibid.*, I, 432.

[14] Second Lieutenant Charles F. L. Durand, Sixth Infantry. *Ibid.*, I, 390.

[15] Surgeon's Mate William H. Nicoll, Sixth Infantry. *Ibid.*, I, 748.

[16] Captain Thomas M. Read, Sixth Infantry. *Ibid.*, I, 819.

[17] First Lieutenant John Ellison, Sixth Infantry. *Ibid.*, I, 403.

[18] This might be Peter Ranne (Ramey) or his son Nathan, both of St. Louis, or Peter Ranne (Rannee), who later traveled with Jedediah Smith through the Rocky Mountains. Houck, *History of Missouri*, II, 56; Morgan, *Jedediah Smith*, 194, 204, 267. It could also be Thomas Riney, Matthew Ramey, or William Ramy. Thomas M. Marshall (ed.), *The Life & Papers of Frederick Bates*, II, 235, 285; Osgood, *Field Notes*, 11 n.

[19] Captain Thomas Hamilton, Sixth Infantry. Heitman, *Historical Register*, I, 494.

[20] Second Lieutenant John Mansfield, Sixth Infantry. *Ibid.*, I, 688.

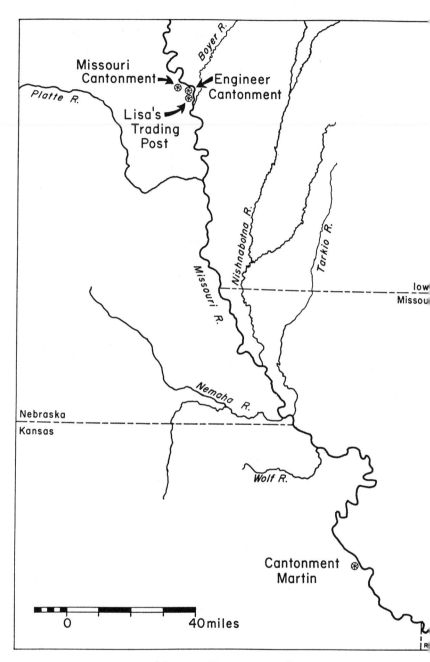

Missouri Cantonment

Boyer R.

Engineer Cantonment

Platte R.

Lisa's Trading Post

Nishnabotna R.

Tarkio R.

Missouri R.

Iowa
Missouri

Nemaha R.

Nebraska

Kansas

Wolf R.

Cantonment Martin

0   40 miles

MISSOURI EXPEDITION, 1819

[45] The Flotilla proceeded about 7 miles and encamped opposite the outlet of a pond on the North which rises and falls with
the Missouri. In this lake are a variety of fine fish, numerous
aquatic fowl and beaver. Lieut Clark with a small party remains
in charge of the stores and provisions at Martin Cantonment for
which we have no transportation.

September 6, 1819—Monday: Passed on the North side an outlet from Goslin lake seven miles in length. In this lake are a
species of nut vulgarly called water Chincopin,[21] numerous soft
shelled turtle cat and Buffaloe fish. Nine miles farther passed 4th
of July Creek[22] on the south and encamped at the head of a small
Island a mile below Independence Creek having made 14 miles.

September 7, 1819—Tuesday: Passed Independence Creek at
the foot of the Old Kansa Village on the South which stood in the
midst of a Prairie surrounded by high hills. The remains of this
village are still to be seen. Made 8 miles and encamped near Yellow Ochre Creek[23] on the South and opposite to a lake on the
North distance half a mile from the River. A few miles above
which are two other lakes in the same bottom of considerable
extent. Much frequented by Elk Swan Geese ducks &c.

September 8, 1819—Wednesday: Passed Yellow Ochre Creek
and six miles above an Island of considerable magnitude on the
North near the head of which we encamped under a perpendicular bank. Made but seven miles in consequence of a delay
occasioned by Lieut Kavanaugh having run a snag through his
boat.

September 9, 1819—Thursday: The order of the Flotilla was
reversed the Infantry proceeding in front. Made seven miles and

21 A variety of shrub or tree related to the chestnut and having an edible nut.
Funk & Wagnall's Dictionary, 468.

22 This is probably Whiskey Creek, which enters the Missouri one mile south
of Atchison, Kansas. It is not to be confused with Independence Creek, several
miles farther upstream.

23 This is now Brush Creek, Doniphan County, Kansas.

encamped at Reevy's Prairie[24] on the North immediately above a circular bend in the river ten miles in circumference and only four hundred [yards] at the base.[25] Thus after more than a days travel we have advanced in longitude but four hundred yards. Capt [John] O Fallon Sutler [left] from Martin Cantonment yesterday overtook us this evening on his way to Council Bluffs by land.

September 10, 1819—Friday: [46] Proceeded as usual at Reveillie. Passed St Michaels Prairie[26] on the North at the distance of five miles above which are some high perpendicular yellow bluffs and encamped above them on the South having made eight miles. St. Michaels Prairie approaches the river on the North at the head of an extensive bottom of excellent land commencing at the upper extremity of Isle des Vaches. This bottom is in many places ten miles in breadth enclosing several lakes with high banks covered with timber which extends nearly to the little river Platte. The Platte by a circuitous bend approaches at St Michaels Prairie within six miles of the Missouri.

September 11, 1819—Saturday: Passed Ordways creek[27] on the North. Made 10 miles and encamped at the lower end of the Big Nodawa Island[28] said to be the largest in the Missouri. This Island is found on the North side well timbered. Near the upper end of which the river Nodawa comes in from the North about eighty yards wide. Navigable some distance up.

September 12, 1819—Sunday: Passed the little Nodawa[29] and

24 This is French Bottom, northeast of St. Joseph, Missouri.

25 There are several loops in the river channel near St. Joseph, Missouri, but because of the frequent shifts of the river, there is no way to know which, if any, of these is being described.

26 This is the bottom land west of the river across from the boundary of Andrew and Buchanan counties, Missouri.

27 A small creek in Andrew County, Missouri. This stream was named by Lewis and Clark for Sergeant John Ordway of their party. Coues, *Lewis and Clark*, I, 41.

28 The bottom land surrounding Garlich Lake in Andrew County, Missouri, was then part of this island.

29 A small island near the tip of Big Nodaway Island.

another Island and encamped at the distance of seven miles at the upper end of the Big Nodawa Island opposite an Island in the Middle of the river.

September 13, 1819—Monday: Passed the outlet of Pike pond[30] on the North and Monters Creek[31] on the South. Made eight miles and encamped above an Island on the South.

September 14, 1819—Tuesday: [Passed] Loup river[32] 40 yards wide coming in from the South opposite an Island on the North and a little below a Prairie on the South in rear of which are some bald hills. Also passed Pape's Creek[33] fifteen yards wide coming in from the South and halted opposite Solomans Island[34] after having made ten miles. Saw several gangs of pelicans and geese and procured a species of Osage plums ripe.

September 15, 1819—Wednesday: Remained opposite Solomans Island this day for the purpose of hunting and washing. The hunters brought in 15 deer and some geese.

September 16, 1819—Thursday: Four miles above Solomons Island passed some yelloe bluffs on the South. Three miles farther Tarkio Creek[35] on the North coming in from behind a willow bar. Three miles farther passed the Nemahaw river,[36] coming in [from] the South opposite an Island on the North [47] at a point where the river is much intersected by sand bars. This river in high water is about eighty yards wide at its mouth. The woodland

30 This pond was near the river in western Holt County, Missouri. William Clark gave it this name because some of his men reported seeing many pike there. Thwaites, *Original Journals*, I, 72.

31 One of several small creeks between the Nodaway and Wolf rivers in Doniphan County, Kansas.

32 The Loup or Wolf River enters the Missouri in Doniphan County, Kansas.

33 Sometimes given as Pappie Creek, this is either Cedar or Squaw Creek in Doniphan County, Kansas. Coues, *Lewis and Clark*, I, 42n.; Osgood, *Field Notes*, 75n.

34 This island no longer exists.

35 Little Tarkio Creek flows through several channels into the Missouri in Holt County, Missouri.

36 The Big Nemaha River joins the Missouri about one mile south of Rulo, Richardson County, Kansas.

ceases at the confluence of the Nemahaw and a beautiful undulating prairie commences covered with verdue. Two miles
farther passed Big Tarkio Creek[37] coming in from the north at
a place formerly called the Island of St. Joseph,[38] but which is
now joined to the North shore. A little above this creek passed a
beautiful level prairie on the South surrounded in rear by hills
covered only with grass which appears like a species of Timothy.
This part of the Missouri appears more picturesque than any
other part which we have passed. The adjacent country is diversi-
fied by hills and dales and intersected with creeks and rivers.
Encamped on the South at the head of a prairie where the hills
approach the river having made by sailing 14 miles.

September 17, 1819—Friday: Proceeded at Reveillie with a
fair wind. At the distance of eight miles passed an island and encamped having made 14 miles in view of a beautiful prairie on
the North. Several of Capt Grays men narrowly escaped drown-
ing in crossing sluices with the cordell. Deer continue plenty.
Two elk and a bear have been killed. A channell of the Missouri
appears to have assumed a different appearance more interrupted
by sand bars and less rapid.

September 18, 1819—Saturday: At the distance of two miles
breakfasted at the head of a prairie on the North of which we
came in view last night. It extended to the hills in rear about five
miles clear of timber and is a perfect plain. At this place Lieut
Keith fainted and fell overboard and was with difficulty saved.
At the distance of four miles passed an Island on the North.
At the distance of ten miles passed Neeshnabatona river[39] fifty

37 The Tarkio River enters the Missouri about three miles southwest of Craig,
Holt County, Missouri.

38 This had been an island caused by river action, but, by 1804, Lewis and Clark
had noted that it was attached to the shore. Here is another example of the
journalist using their account. Coues, *Lewis and Clark*, I, 44.

39 The Nishnabotna River has changed its course since 1819. Then it entered
the Missouri about ten miles south of Rockport, Atchison County, Missouri. The
Nemaha Quadrangle, 1915, clearly shows this older channel. At present this stream

yards wide coming in from the North. Three miles above encamped on the South having made 13 miles near some old trading houses on the North having made by sailing 14 miles.[40]

September 19, 1819—Sunday: At the distance of four miles passed the Little Nemahaw[41] coming in from the South 48 yards wide. Above which a large beautiful prairie on the same side extending a great distance along the river bounded in extent in rear only by the horizon below which the [48] approach [of] the river broken and bare. Capt. Grays Hunters for the officers mess came in this morning having killed six deer and a large black bear which they hung up on the shore but excaped our notice. At the distance of eight miles farther passed a small island on the South at the upper extremity of which we encamped near a range of bald precipitous hills on the same side of which approached the river. Made 12 miles.

September 20, 1819—Monday: At the distance of three miles passed an island called Fair Sun[42] on the South side of which we proceeded. Saw on the banks this morning a quantity of the Carduus Benedictus[43] in bloom, also the wild Been which appears ripe. At the distance of eight miles farther made an island on the South called Bald Pated Island a large and beautiful Prairie and some elevated and bare hills on the North Called Bald Pated Hills and Prairie.[44] Made eleven miles and encamped on the North opposite the middle of Bald Island at a point where the Nichnabatona river approaches within 200 yards of the Missouri and immediately turns away [at] the foot of the Bald Hills.

enters the Missouri about twenty-five miles above at McKissock Island, Nemaha County, Nebraska.

[40] The phrase "having made by sailing 14 miles" is an error. It repeats the last phrase of the September 16 entry and supports the contention that the journal is being copied from notes.

[41] The Little Nemaha River enters the Missouri at Nemaha, Nebraska.

[42] This was in the vicinity of Peru, Nemaha County, Nebraska.

[43] This was a variety of wild thistle, perhaps the hooded thistle.

[44] Bald Pated Island was in the vicinity of McKissock Island in Nemaha County, Nebraska. The Bald Pated Hills are about one mile to the east in Atchison County, Missouri. Bald Pated Prairie extends along the river bottoms.

September 21, 1819—Tuesday: Captain Gray broke the yard arm of his boat in consequence of which the Flotilla was detained until a new one was made when we commenced sailing and at the distance of 13 miles passed an island on the North opposite a point where the hills approach the river on the South. One mile above which the same bluffs overhang the river composed of indurated clay and sand stone intermixed with carbonated vegetables. The soil at this point appears coloured with the oxide of iron. Some salt appears concreted on the surface resembling Sulphate of Alum and Nitrat of Potash. Several of mineral coal also were found on the shore.[45] Encamped on the North side near the lower point of Oven Islands[46]—two in number. One in the middle of the river the other on the South shore opposite Terriens prairie[47] on the North and at an old trading house in ruins.[48] Made 17 Miles. We were this day detained three hours by Major Foster and Lieut Scott whose [boat] ran upon a log lying under water. Saw some geese pelicans.

September 22, 1819—Wednesday: At the distance of one mile passed Oven Islands. Four miles farther made an island on the North above which we [49] encamped on the South at some high hills destitute of wood which approached the river. Saw some grouse ducks and paraquets. Made 12 miles.

September 23, 1819—Thursday: Progressed but 4 miles. Encamped at Weeping Water Creek[49] on the South 30 yards wide having been detained by Northwest winds. The current of the

45 Here the writer takes more than his usual interest in minerals. This may indicate that he had been talking with Mr. Jessup, the geologist, or other members of Major Long's party of scientists.

46 There are several small islands about three miles south of Nebraska City, which might be those referred to here.

47 Bakers Oven or Pie Oven seems more accurate. Coues, *Lewis and Clark,* I, 48–49n.; Osgood, *Field Notes,* 82n.; Thwaites, *Original Journals,* I, 83.

48 This was either a fur trading establishment or a temporary shelter for riverboat crews, because Lewis and Clark do not mention it. Coues, *Lewis and Clark,* I, 49.

49 This enters the Missouri in Otoe County, Nebraska.

Missouri by observation appears to be fifty feet in forty five seconds. Col. Morgan was this day arrested.[50]

September 24, 1819—Friday: Made 6 miles and encamped for the day. Detained by strong Northwest winds. One of Capt Magee's men was this day accidentally killed by the discharge of a rifle.[51]

September 25, 1819—Saturday: At the distance of eight miles passed an island above which the corpse of the man who was killed yesterday was interred at the base of some high bare hills which approached the river on the South. Made but 11 miles in consequence of mistaking the Channel and returning.

September 26, 1819—Sunday: At the distance of 12 miles passed the river Platte[52] coming in from the South 600 miles above the Confluence of the Missouri with the Mississippi and 600 yards wide at the mouth. The hills which have approached the Missouri on the south for the distance of ten miles below the Platte near its mouth suddenly cease and the land becomes low. The current of the Platte near its mouth is said to be more rapid than the Missouri and is at its mouth much intersected by sand bars. The water which issues from the Platte at this time is limpid but at some seasons is very muddy and adds much to the turbidness of the Missouri. Three miles above the Platte passed two trading boats and a few Ottoe Indians near Butterfly creek[53] on the South 18 yards wide and encamped one mile above them on the North having made 16 miles. The timber near the Missouri consist principally of Oak hickory Elm & Cotton wood. The hazle nuts which are abundant in the prairies are ripe. The grass

---

[50] This was the result of a minor dispute, because there is no record of the arrest. Ninth Military Department Orders, Records of United States Army Commands, Record Group 98, National Archives.

[51] Atkinson's response to this death was prompt. He ordered all unauthorized use of firearms to cease (see Appendix, item # 25).

[52] The Platte joins the Missouri from the west, one mile north of Plattsmouth, Nebraska.

[53] This is Papillion Creek, which enters the Missouri about two miles north of the Platte in Sarpy County, Nebraska.

is brown and dry and the hills on the North which are destitute of timber are on fire. Deer have become scarce but ducks and geese more plenty. Saw some large blue heron.

September 27, 1819—Monday: At the distance of six miles passed Musquito Creek[54] on the [50] North just below a beautiful elevated level and extensive prairie on the same side. Doc. Malone and Dr Jessup left the Flotilla this morning to proceed to the Council Bluffs by land. Three return boats passed us for St. Louis. Made 17 miles and encamped on the South a little below a pond much frequented by aquatic fowl and opposite a large prairie on the North which extends to some high hills in view from the encampment. The geese on the sand bars more numerous.

September 28, 1819—Tuesday: Passed this morning an extensive prairie on the South at the head of which we breakfasted. Where Dr Malone who abandoned the intention of proceeding to Council Bluffs on foot joined us having seen the pond above our last nights encampment which we did not discover. Immediately after breakfast passed an extensive range of barren brown and bare hills on the North the bases of which in many places are broken by the current of the Missouri. These are the first hills which approach the Missouri on the north above the Nodawa. At the distance of 14 miles came to some high perpendicular yellow Bluffs on the South where Captain [John] O Fallon met us from Manuel Lisa's establishment which place he informs us is but three and a half miles by land and nine miles by water.

Near this place a bee hive was found and several ducks and turkies killed below. On the same side is the remains of a small establishment[55] and evident signs that the land has been culti-

54 Mosquito Creek joins the Missouri in Mills County, Iowa.

55 This was probably a fur-trade post. There were so many traders operating along the Missouri that it is not possible to determine whose post this may have been.

vated. The prairies on the South below this place are on fire. Three miles farther encamped on the North side having made 17 miles.

September 29, 1819—Wednesday: Passed some hills on the North which suddenly leave the river below a large prairie, and some low land on the south covered with small cotton trees and at the distance of six miles made Manuel Lisa's establ. Situated below some hills on the south and two miles above Bowyers River[56] coming in from the North 30 yards wide a little above the mouth which is much impeded by sand bars [51] and enters the Missouri through several different channels. On our arrival at this place a board of Officers was appointed by Col Atkinson consisting of Col Chambers and Capt Martin of the Rifle Regt Major Humphreys and Capt Hamilton of the Infantry and Major Biddle acting Asst Adjutant Genl to examine the adjacent country and report the most eligible spot for Cantoning.

On our Arrival we found that Maj Long had commenced building winter quarters for his command about one mile above Mr Lisas establishment where is a safe harbor for his Steamboat.[57] Eighty head of Cattle for the troops have arrived.

Maj. [Benjamin] O Fallon Indian Agent has sent express to the Pauanies to demand restitution of the articles taken from Maj Biddle and Party also the Indians who took prisoners two Americans on the Arkansas and detained them untill ransomed by Mr Immel[58] a trader on this river. News has arrived that a keel boat laden with provisions has [been] lost near Grand River and that the Steam boat Johnson is disabled above the Kansas, and unable to proceed.

56 Boyer River enters the Missouri in Pottawattamie County, Iowa.

57 Major Long's party built cabins on the west bank of the Missouri, north of Fort Lisa, which they called Engineer Cantonment. Thwaites, *James Account*, I, 221; Poesch, *Titian R. Peale*, 27.

58 Michael Immell (sometimes spelled Immel) was a St. Louis fur trader associated with the Missouri Fur Company. In 1823 he was killed by the Blackfeet. Chittenden, *American Fur Trade*, I, 158; Oglesby, *Manuel Lisa*, 141, 175, 187; Heitman, *Historical Register*, I, 562.

September 30, 1819—Thursday: Mr Manuel Lisa and Lady arrived this day from St. Louis which was announced by the firing of swivles from his works vis a stockade. Our men are in tents but the boats are not unladen. Doct Gale Lieut Scott & Capt Livingston went on a hunting excursion up the Bowyer but saw no game.

October 1, 1819—Friday: [52] Prairies Still on fire. Large quantities of honey has been found and quantities of Grapes and hazel Nuts are daily brought in. The Flotilla is waiting for the report of the Board of Officers who are searching for a suitable place to encamp during the winter.

October 2, 1819—Saturday: The flotilla left their encampment and proceed three miles above Council Bluffs to a Cottonwood grove on the South which is reported to be the most eligible place for Cantoning. Made 12 miles.

PART IV

Cantonment Missouri
1819-1820

October 3, 1819—Sunday: The troops are engaged clearing a place for their tents pitching them and unloading the boats.

October 4, 1819—Monday: Maj [Benjamin] O Fallon had a Council with about two hundred Indians[1] at Maj Longs establishment. The Pauanies are daily expected. The troops this day commence cutting timber for the cantonment.

October 5, 1819—Tuesday: The Prairies are still on fire. Duck Gees & Brant[2] are the only game our hunters bring in.

October 9, 1819—Saturday: A council was held at Maj Longs estabt with the Pauanees who came in Yesterday. Most of the Gentlemen from the Cantonment attended. The Indians promised to punish those who robbed Maj Biddle and party and to return the articles which they had taken.

October 10, 1819—Sunday: Major Long and Doct Jessup of the Engineers left this for Philadelphia.[3] The principal Pauanies arrived in Camp on which occasion a salute was fired.

October 12, 1819—Tuesday: Capt Bliss[4] and Lady arrived at Camp Missouri in a Keel boat laden with provisions.

1 These included men from the Oto, Missouri, and Iowa tribes. Thwaites, *James Account,* I, 238–39.
2 This is a ducklike waterfowl.
3 Jesup resigned, and Long visited his family in Philadelphia before returning to Washington for new orders. Wood, *Stephen H. Long,* 84; Thwaites, *James Account,* I, 249–50.
4 Captain John Bliss, Sixth Infantry. Heitman, *Historical Register,* I, 225.

October 13, 1819—Wednesday: Lieut Gantt[5] of the Rifle Regt arrived from St Louis by land. He had been lost with his party seven days.

October 13, 1819[6]—Wednesday: A Court Martial convened for the trial of Lieut Scott[7] who was lately arrested [by] Col Morgan.

October 16, 1819—Saturday: Lieut Keeler[8] of the Infantry arrived by land from the River Platte, Near which the boat on which he was on board ran on a snag and sank, laden with ordnance stores Cannon &c Cargo valuable.

October 18, 1819—Monday: Lieut Mix[9] of the Infantry arrived by land having been lost and remained five days without food. [53] Lieut Keeler went down the river in a Keelboat to attempt raising some of the stores which were sunk near the Platte.

October 20, 1819—Wednesday: The first load of stone brought from a quarry about ten miles below this place arrived for the construction of chimneys. Lieut L. Palmer of the Infy and Lieut Campbell[10] of the Rifle Regiment arrived with provisions from the Steam boat which wrecked her works above the Kansas River.

A Soldier who was missing last night was found this morning partially consumed by the wolves about 90 yds from Camp. Supposed to have been killed in a fight.

October 21, 1819—Thursday: Capt Livingston who is after stone at the quarry had the misfortune to sink his boat by the waves rollin[g] into her during the while loaded.

5 First Lieutenant John Gantt, Rifle Regiment. *Ibid.*, I, 444.

6 This may be a mistake because there is already an entry for this date, but the script is clear and does show October 13.

7 This was the result of a petty quarrel while at Martin Cantonment. Scott was charged and found guilty of conduct unbecoming an officer. Ninth Military Department Orders, 1819, RG 98.

8 First Lieutenant Samuel Keeler, Jr., Sixth Infantry. Heitman, *Historical Register*, I, 587.

9 Second Lieutenant William A. Mix, Sixth Infantry. *Ibid.*, I, 718.

10 First Lieutenant Daniel H. Campbell, Rifle Regiment. *Ibid.*, I, 277.

October 27, 1819—Wednesday: Col. Atkinson gave a dinner to the Gentlemen of each Regiment. Major Ketchum arrived with the boat which Capt Livingston sunk on the 21st.

October 28, 1819—Thursday: Major Biddle Asst. Adjt. General arrived from a visit to a lodge of Indians with 6 Horses which he had purchased for the use of the Public. Capt. Shaylor[11] and Lieut Brown[12] arrived from Johnstons steam boat in a keel boat laden with provision. A boat of Mr Greens[13] also arrived with provisions. Mr. Patrick arrived with 200 head of Cattle for the use of the Troops.

October 30, 1819—Saturday: Lieut Clarke with four boats arrived from Martin Cantonment with the Stores which had been left there. That post is evacuated.

October 31, 1819—Sunday: Lieut Field with a party of ten men left this for Chariton to stake out a direct rout through the Country. Major Biddle Actg Asst. Inspecting General Mustered & Inspected the Troops at this post.

November 1, 1819—Monday: A Dinner was given by the Brigade to Col. Atkinson.

November 2, 1819—Tuesday: Col. Atkinson Col. Chambers, Major Biddle, & Major Smith[14] left this place in the General Smith for Saint Louis & Lieut Col. Morgan assumed the Command. Lieut Keith & Lieut Campbell also left this for St. Louis.

November 10, 1819—Wednesday: Lieut Wilcox[15] Lieut Bedel[16] and Doctor Mower[17] of the Infty arrived in a Keelboat from the Steam boat Johnston which wrecked her works.

11 Captain Ephraim Shaylor, Sixth Infantry. In 1818 he changed his name to Shaler. *Ibid.*, I, 878.

12 First Lieutenant Jacob Brown, Sixth Infantry. This is not Jacob Brown, Jr., son of the commanding general of the army. *Ibid.*, I, 252.

13 This individual is not identifiable.

14 Captain (brevet major) Gerard D. Smith, Sixth Infantry. Heitman, *Historical Register*, I, 898.

15 First Lieutenant De Lafayette Wilcox, Sixth Infantry. *Ibid.*, I, 1034.

16 First Lieutenant Hazen Bedel, Sixth Infantry. *Ibid.*, I, 205.

17 Surgeon Thomas G. Mower, Sixth Infantry. *Ibid.*, I, 733.

79

November 14, 1819—Sunday: Capt. Hale[18] and Lieut Mc-Alvin[19] of the Infantry arrived from the steam boat Johnston with provisions and men among whom are the Band of the Infty.

November 20, 1819—Saturday: Capt [John] O Fallon left this place for Washington having previously paid the troops.

November 23, 1819—Tuesday: The rifle Regt removed to their quarters, and received a complimentary Order, from Lt Col. Morgan comdg. for their industry in contructing them.

November 24, 1819—Wednesday: A soldier of Capt. Armstrong's company Rifle Regt named Shindon,[20] shot himself with his rifle after a fit of intoxication.

[54–55] Diagram of Cantonment Missouri.

December 21, 1819—Tuesday: [56] Mr. Keer[21] agent of the Sutler arrived from St Louis. He had charge of a boat laden with goods, which in consequence of the ice he left it at Isle des Vache in charge of the Capt. of the Steam boat Johnston, which winters there.

December 24, 1819—Friday: Most of the Infantry are in quarters.

December 25, 1819—Saturday: Capt. Reed of the Infantry died after a short illness leaving a widow and one child. He was distinguished as an enterprising and efficient officer during the last war.

December 30, 1819—Thursday: Capt. Magee arrived, from the

18 Captain William F. Hail, Sixth Infantry. *Ibid.*, I, 486.

19 First Lieutenant James McIlvaine, Sixth Infantry. *Ibid.*, I, 668.

20 This is a mistake. There is no such individual listed on the muster rolls of the regiment in 1819. This may be Joseph Stidson, Daniel Sheridan, John Sandlon, or Randolph Sandlon. Muster Rolls, Rifle Regiment, 1819, Records of the Office of the Adjutant General, RG 94.

21 This is Peter Keer, an employee of John O'Fallon. *St. Louis Enquirer,* September 29, 1819.

Nodawa, where he had been hunting, and took command of the Regiment of Riflemen.

December 31, 1819—Friday: Lt. Col. Morgan mustered and inspected the Brigade.

January 4, 1820—Tuesday: Lt. Field arrived from Franklin in company with Lt. Wickliff[22] of the Infantry, After rectifying a line of communication between Franklin and Cantonment Missouri.[23] The country through which he passed consists principally of prairie interspursed with copse of wood. His estimate of distance between the two places is three hundred and twenty miles, in a course from the Cantonment south East.

January 10, 1820—Monday: The troops are sickly; affected principally by scurvy.[24]

February 15, 1820—Tuesday: A Buffaloe was killed near the Cantonment by corporal Key of Capt. Martin's company.[25]

February 16, 1820—Wednesday: Maj. Ketchum, Capt. Magee several others officers of the command went up to Sioux river about 30 miles for the purpose of killing Buffaloe but returned on the 21st having seen but one.

February 22, 1820—Tuesday: Was celebrated by a dinner and Ball in commemoration of the auspicious day which gave birth to a Washington.

February 25, 1820—Friday: [57] Mr. Dougherty[26] of the In-

---

22 Second Lieutenant William N. Wickliff, Sixth Infantry. Heitman, *Historical Register*, I, 1033.

23 Field and his party of ten had left the camp on October 31 to survey an overland route to Chariton, Missouri Territory. His report is filed in Secretary of War, Letters Received, Unregistered Series. Record Group 107, Records of the Office of the Secretary of War.

24 Here the journal assumes a more medical character. Gale makes frequent notes about the sickness at the post and in January begins using the journal as a letter book for his medical correspondence.

25 Corporal Henry Key, Rifle Regiment. Muster Rolls, 1819, AGO, RG, 94.

26 John Dougherty was a sub-agent under Benjamin O'Fallon.

dian department Mr. Peal[27] & several gentlemen of the Engineer Steam boat, who went to the Sioux river[28] hunting on the 15th returned having killed thirteen Buffaloe.

February 26, 1820—Saturday: A board of war consisting of Maj. Humphreys, Maj. Foster & Capt. Magee, who have been devising means for the relief of the command who are severely scurged with scurvey, report in favor of sending the sick to the neighborhood of the settlements, where proper sustenance can be procured for them.[29]

February 28, 1820—Monday: Lt. Field with a party are sent out on express to St. Louis on his new route.

February 29, 1820—Tuesday: Col. Morgan Mustered and inspected the troops. There are two hundred and eighty sick principally with the scurvy. Capt. Bissel and a rifleman returned from a Buffaloe hunt having killed four. Elk are daily killed near the Cantonment.

March 9, 1820—Thursday: Maj. [Benjamin] O Fallon, Lt. Gantt & Dr. Meloan returned from a Buffaloe hunt, having killed five and seen numerous herd, which they left unmolested having no means of transporting them to the Cantont.

March 10, 1820—Friday: Lt. Allison of the 6th Infantry who died yesterday was buried with the usual honors of war escorted by all the officers & band. Six soldiers were also buried to day. Sickness continues fatel. Three hundred and sixty are on the sick report.

March 15, 1820—Wednesday: A party of soldiers returned from a hunting excursion after killing 14 buffaloe having seen large droves which induced Capt Magee Magee[30] to ascend the river for the purpose of killing and jerking their meat.

27 This is Titian R. Peale, assistant naturalist of Long's party.
28 The Little Sioux River enters the Missouri in Harrison County, Iowa.
29 This remedy is one suggested by Gale in his letter to the board of February 25, 1820 (see Appendix, item # 34).

March 16, 1820—Thursday: Maj. Humphreys & Lt Saniford went out on a Buffaloe hunt.

March 16, 1820[31]*—Thursday:* [58] Lt. Clarke who was killed yesterday in a duel was intered with Military honors.[32]

March 19, 1820—Sunday: Maj. Ketcham, who has been employed with a command in extricating the boats from the ice at the Engineer Cantonment arrived with one of them. Capt. Gray proceeds to St. Louis in a canoe for the recovery of his health.

[Temporary End of Journal][33] [Pages 58–71 letters]

March 25, 1820—Saturday: [71] Major Ketchum Lieut McIlvain, Lieut [name illegible][34] Lieut McCray, Doctor Nicholl and Doctor Malone, descended the River in Four Boats to Fort Osage with Eighty sick Riflemen and Twenty Sick Infantry. Captain Boardman and Family Captain Gray and Mr Potts also went down the River.

April 1, 1820—Saturday: [72] Captain Magee arrived from a Buffaloe hunt. He had loaded two Rafts with Meat which were lost in descending the River. Two Men were Drowned.

Lieut. Field arrived express from St Louis.

The Scurvy which has been so Fatal amongst the Troops has become less troublesome. Sixty Riflemen one hundred Infantry

---

30 The second Magee is a copying error.

31 The second entry for March 16, 1820, is probably because it begins a new page in the manuscript.

32 There is no evidence which shows with whom this duel was fought or why.

33 Except for a few scattered, small entries, the next thirteen pages of the journal (58–71) have been used by Dr. Gale as a letter book for his medical correspondence. The letters are with the appended material, with the exception of the following: John Gale to Matthew Magee, February 20, 1820, p. 58; John Gale to Matthew Magee, February 20, 1820, pp. 58–60; John Gale to Willoughby Morgan, April 5, 1820, p. 72; John Gale to Willoughby Morgan, April 28, 1820, p. 73. These items have been deleted because they repeat material in the other letters.

34 This name is crowded into the margin, and the first four letters appear to be "Purm." There is no officer at the post whose name includes any such combination of letters.

died of this complaint. Wild Vegetables have appeared. The Sick are confined principally to the woods to subsist on game.

April 10, 1820—Monday: A Boat of Mr Manuels passed this for the Sioux. Captain Magee accompanied it.

April 13, 1820—Thursday: [73] A man of Captain Magees Company named Thomas[35] terminated his existince with his Rifle.

Mr Manuel and Family left this on the 5th April for St Louis in a Skiff.

April 28, 1820—Friday: A Boat arrived from Franklin. Mr Curtis owner. Loaded with Potatoes and Bacon. Three Boats passed from the Mandans laden with Buffaloe Robes and [one word illegible].[36]

May 4, 1820—Thursday: An Express arrived from Franklin with intelligence that Congress had refused to make any further appropriation for the Missouri Expedition under the impression that the views of Government may be realised by an established post at this place. Missouri Territory has been admitted into the union without restriction relating to slaves.[37]

May 6, 1820—Saturday: Maj [Benjamin] O Fallon Indian Agent and Captain Riley and party arrived from their visit to the Pawanies with sixty Mules and Horses—Twenty public—Forty private property. Also two Buffaloe calves taken in the prairie.

May 6, 1820[38]—Saturday: [74] The Pawanies were lately overtaken in a prairie by a party of Spaniards from whom they had stolen Horses. All were killed or surrendered amounting to one

35 Private Martin Thomas, Rifle Regiment. Muster Rolls, 1819, AGO, RG, 94.

36 This appears to be To - - gs, but even those letters are unclear.

37 This refers to the Missouri Enabling Act, passed on March 6, 1820. Missouri did not enter the Union for more than a year because of the slavery controversy. *U. S. Statutes at Large,* III, 545–48; *Niles Register* (Baltimore), August 18, 1821.

38 This second May 6 entry begins on a new page, which explains why a second heading is used.

Hundred.[39] One of the hunters came in who killed an Antelope yesterday. Mr Patrick arrived from Franklin with One Hundred and Eighty head of Cattle for the Troops.

May 11, 1820—Thursday: A party of Indians took two Horses from Mr Manuel and fired on the Flotilla.

May 12, 1820—Friday: Mr Patrick who started yesterday for St. Louis returned having lost his Horses by the Indians. A Clerk to the Sutler arrived yesterday From St. Louis. He was pursued by the Indians but escaped. Their object his Horses, & appeared to be Sacks.

May 18, 1820—Thursday: Mr Immel arrived from the trading establishments above. Capt Magee passanger. The Indians had robbed Two Traiding Houses and stripped the Clerks of their wearing apparel. In descending the River he had the misfortune to loose Peltry to the amount of Five Thousand Dollars by running his Boat on a snag.

May 21, 1820—Sunday: Mr Prate[40] arrived with Peltry. While on his [way] from one of his trading houses to his Boat he was attacked by a party of Indians supposed to be Sacks. One of his men killed and Three wounded by the first fire. The Indians succeeded in taking his Horses nine in number with a few other articles and escaped. Three wounded men succeeded in gaining the Boat.

May 22, 1820—Monday: Captain Magee and Doctor Gale with a party of 20 Men accompanied by Mr Pratt proceeded to the Mahar Village near which the Fight occured for the purpose of burying the man who was killed and recovering the Peltry which the Indians were unable to carry away. The party returned on the

39 There were frequent skirmishes between the Spanish from Santa Fe and the Plains Indians. According to Stephen Long, the Pawnees had many Spanish prisoners. Thwaites, *James Account*, II, 160 ff.

40 Mr. Bernard Pratte, Sr., was a prominent St. Louis fur trader and businessman. Bernard Pratte, Jr., "Reminiscences of Gen. Bernard Pratte, Jr.," *Missouri Historical Society Bulletin*, Vol. VI (Oct., 1949), 60.

30th May, having found and buried the dead man, recovered one of the Horses and the Peltry.

May 29, 1820—Monday: Major Long and Captain Bell of the Artillery arrived, from Washington.[41]

June 1, 1820—Thursday: [75] A dinner was given to Major Long and party by the Rifle Regt.

June 5, 1820—Monday: Major Long with the exploring expedition set out on their way to the head waters of the Platt and Arkansaw, which they are to descend in divided parties.

June 6, 1820—Tuesday: Captain Martin and Lieut Conant[42] arrived with three Boats from Fort Osage, with a part of the sick who are recovered which were sent to that place under Major Ketchum. They report that all are recovering.

June 10, 1820—Saturday: The Steam Boat Engineer under Lieutenant Graham descended to the mouth of the Arkinsaw to wait Major Longs arrival.

June 11, 1820—Sunday: The River has risen to such a height as to overflow the Country adjacent to the Barracks. The water is prevented from coming into the Barracks by banking up the Gate ways. The bank has fallen in to such an extent that we have been compelled to take away the Sutlers Store, Blacksmith Shop and several other out houses to prevent their falling into the River.

June 12, 1820—Monday: This morning the water is one foot deep in the Cantonment and continues to rise. The Troops are ordered to repair in boats to the Council Bluffs. All are busily employed in removing in the boats.

41 Captain John R. Bell, Light Artillery. Heitman, *Historical Register,* I, 208. Long brought new orders from Secretary of War Calhoun. The Scientific Expedition was to abandon the *Western Engineer* and instead was to travel by land to the source of the Platte. Then they were to travel down the Arkansas and Red rivers to the Mississippi. Thwaites, *James Account,* II, 189–90.

42 Second Lieutenant Roswell Conant, Rifle Regiment. Heitman, *Historical Register,* I, 320.

June 13, 1820—Tuesday: Our encampment was formed on the Council Bluffs.

The river has risen during the last night to such an height that the water rushes in at the windows of the Cantonment which we left yesterday. A quantity of Salt & flour are lost by the inundation, which [76] we had not time to remove. Colonels Atkinson & Chambers, Major[s] Biddle and Smith, Capts. Kearney[43] & Whitman[44] pay Mr. arrived from St. Louis.

June 17, 1820—Saturday: The Cannon & even their carriages at Cantonment Missouri are covered with water & the front row of barracks are falling into the river.[45]

July 1, 1820—Saturday: The water of the Missouri is falling, leaving a deposit of sand in the Cantonment of two feet.

July 2, 1820—Sunday: Captain Magee set out for the Mouth of the St Peters, with a party of twenty men, for the purpose of making a road.[46] Lt. Col. Morgan Capt. Kearney Lieuts. Talcott[47] & Pentland accompanied him.

July 4, 1820—Tuesday: The day was ushered in with a National Salute. At 10 OClock the troops were reviewed by Col Atkinson. At 11 OClock an oration was delivered by Major Biddle. At 3 Oclock the officers sat down to dinner at an arbour prepared for the purpose.

The day passed in mirth & good humor.

[43] Captain Stephen W. Kearny, Second Infantry. He became a brigadier general in 1846, was breveted for gallant conduct during the Mexican War, and served until his death in 1848. *Ibid.,* I, 586.

[44] Captain Alphonso Wetmore, Sixth Infantry. In the journal this name is sometimes spelled Whitman and Witmore. *Ibid,* 1021.

[45] This flood was reported to be the highest experienced along that stretch of the river. Henry Atkinson to Thomas A. Smith, June 20, 1820. Smith Papers, SHSM.

[46] The St. Peters is now the Minnesota River, which enters the Mississippi at Minneapolis–St. Paul. For a discussion of this expedition see Stephen W. Kearny, "Journal of Stephen Watts Kearny" (ed. by Valentine M. Porter), *Missouri Historical Society Collections,* Vol. III (Jan., April, 1908), 99–131.

[47] Second Lieutenant Andrew Talcott, Engineers. Heitman, *Historical Register,* I, 943.

July 6, 1820—Thursday: The first Timber for the erection of the new Cantonment arrived.

July 7, 1820—Friday: [77] Two Boats Laden with provisions arrived from St Louis.

July 8, 1820—Saturday: Capt. Witmore Capt. Bliss & Lady and Mrs. Ketchum & Lieut Conant went in the return boat to St Louis.

July 10, 1820—Monday: Two boats arrived in one of which was Capt Gray. Major Humphreys & Lady & Lieut Staniford & Lady went down the river.

[End of Journal]

[78–79] List of Bedding in Wards No. 1, 2, & 3, 4. Jefferson Barracks hospital, 5th Sept 1830.

[80] Chart showing the same information as the preceeding list.

APPENDIX

Letters and Documents

1. John Calhoun to Thomas Smith[1]

DEPARTMENT OF WAR
March 16, 1818

In order to extend and protect our trade with the Indians, it has been determined to establish a permanent military post at the mouth of the Yellow Stone river. You will take immediate and efficient measures to carry it into effect. The strength of the detachment, the means of transportation, the supplies of provisions, are wholly left under your controul. You will consult with his excellency governor Clark,[2] in relation to the country, with its capacity to supply the wants of the detachment, the navigation of the river, the force and disposition of the tribes of Indians in that quarter, in order to enable you to make your arrangements in such a manner as may be best calculated to effect the object in view.

The post contemplated being very remote, and on that account, exposed in its supplies to many accidents and dangers, it will be necessary after this year, that it should have the means of supply within itself. The reported fertility of the country in that neighbourhood, and the abundance of game, will render this measure, dictated by prudence, very easy. You will draw on this

[1] Secretary of War, Letters Sent, Military Affairs, Vol. 10, RG 107; *The Papers of John C. Calhoun* (ed. by Robert L. Meriwether and W. Edwin Hemphill), II, 194–95.
[2] This is the former explorer William Clark, then territorial governor of Missouri.

department for such expenditures as the nature of the service may render necessary.

It is probable, that the lateness of the season will prevent the detachment from reaching the post contemplated this summer; and in that event, as intermediate posts will probably be required, it will take [a] post at the Mandan village, or at such other point as may be thought advisable . . . .

You will instruct the officer who may be detailed to command the detachment, to use every means to conciliate the Indians, and impress on them the belief, that our intention is friendly towards them. It is expected the English traders will take unusual pains to make a contrary impression. They have great advantages in controuling the savages thro' their commanding station on Red river, and as our contemplated establishment at Yellow Stone, will greatly curtail their trade towards the head of the Missouri, we must expect every opposition from them. No pains must be spared to counteract such efforts . . . .

The remoteness of the post will, in some respects, render it unpleasant to those who may be detailed for the service; but I am persuaded that the American soldier, actuated by the spirit of enterprize, will meet the privations which may be necessary with cheerfulness. Combined with the importance of the service, the glory of planting the American flag at a point so distant, on so noble a river, will not be unfelt. The world will behold in it the mighty growth of our republic, which but a few years since, was limited by the Alleghany; but now is ready to push its civilization and laws to the western confines of the continent.

2. General Order[3]

ADJUTANT AND INSPECTOR GENERAL'S OFFICE
February 8, 1819

. . . The Sixth Infantry now at Plattsburgh in the Northern Division will be marched as soon as practicable to St. Louis in the

3 Adjutant General, Orders and Circulars, Vol. 2, RG 94.

South Division. The Commanding General in the North Division will adopt the measures for carrying this order into effect and will cause the Commanding General of the South Division to be advised of their arrival in his Division, with reports of the munitions, clothing, &c.

The Recruits of the 5th now in Massachusetts will be immediately put in motion to join the Sixth, & march with it if practicable . . . .

3. John Wool to Henry Atkinson[4]

BROWNVILLE, N. Y.
February 8, 1819

In conformity with the enclosed General Order, Major General Brown[5] directs that you prepare with as little delay as may be practicable, your regiment for its destined services, such recruits as have not joined the rendezvous at Greenbush, [New York] where they will be got in readiness to join you on your march. The route which you are to take, and the means of obtaining transportation, will be pointed out to you by the next mail. The Major General expects that you will be in readiness to commence your march in time to reach Pittsburgh by the first day of May next. How far it may be proper to conceal from the privates of your regiment the extent of the movement you are most competent to judge. The Major General, however, presumes it will not be necessary to promulgate the order to its full extent.

4. Henry Atkinson to John Calhoun[6]

GREENBUSH, N. Y.
March 27, 1819

I have the honor to inform you that my Regiment arrived at

4 Northern Division, Letters Sent, Post Revolutionary Commands, Vol. 35 (409), RG 94. This communication is from the headquarters of the Northern Division of the army, not from the Adjutant General's Office in Washington.

5 Major General Jacob Brown commanded the Northern Division of the army from 1815 until 1821 when he became commanding general of the army. Heitman, *Historical Register*, I, 252; *DAB*, III, 124–26.

6 Secretary of War, Letters Received, Registered Series, RG 107.

this post yesterday in good condition; we lost but one man on the march, occasioned by an unfortunate, or rather accidental death. Only two desertions have occured since the order for the march was recd, and to judge from the good spirits manifested by all grades, we shall have a successful movement. I had caused all our supplies to be in readiness on shortest notice, we shall be able to recommence our march as soon as the recruits arrive, who are expected in two days; when, I shall take my departure for Washington City, with a hope of reaching there by the 3rd of April, & at the furthest, by the 5th.

5. *John Calhoun to Henry Atkinson*[7]

DEPARTMENT OF WAR

March 27, 1819

It is a subject of much regret that my departure from Washington will take place before your passage through it to take command of the 9th Military Department. Your command is considered of the first importance and responsibility. The establishment of the contemplated posts on the Missouri have two great objects in view, the enlargement and protection of our fur trade, and the permanent peace of our North Western frontier by the establishment of a decided controul over the various tribes of Indians in that quarter. These objects will indicate the policy which ought to be pursued. To such of our citizens who may conform to the laws and regulations in relation to Indian trade and intercourse, you will extend kindness and protection. In relation to foreign traders who by the Act of Congress are entirely excluded, your conduct in the first instance must be governed by a sound discretion to be exercised in each case. No decisive step ought, perhaps, to be taken till your posts are fully established; and till you feel yourself secure against the effects of hostilities; at which time notice ought to be given that after a fixed period, you will rigidly exclude all trade by foreigners and such as are not authorized by law.

7 Secretary of War, Letters Sent, Military Affairs, Vol. 10, RG 107.

Of the two objects in view, the permanent security of our frontier is considered by far of the greatest importance, and will especially claim your attention. If practicable you will gain the confidence and friendship of all the Indian tribes with whom you may have any intercourse. The Agent for the Missouri has had special instructions in relation to his duties, of which I enclose you a copy.

It will be a great point gained, if the posts can be established without Indian hostilities, and such I confidently believe may be the case with discretion. Undoubtedly the Indians ought to be fully impressed with our capacity to avenge any injury which they may offer us; but it is no less important that they should be equally impressed with our justice and humanity. Should you succeed in convincing them of both, all difficulties will be removed . . . .

You will keep an exact journal of all of your proceedings and report to this Department at short intervals the progress of your movements and such events as may be of importance to be known.

6. Henry Atkinson to Andrew Jackson[8]

PITTSBURGH, PENNSYLVANIA
April 17, 1819

I have the honor to inform you that I arrived at this place [Pittsburgh] the day before yesterday from Washington City, whither I had been ordered to receive final instructions relative to the Missouri expedition, and where I recd. the orders you left for me. I deemed it advisable to preceed my Regiment for the purpose of having transportation & supplies ready against its arrival here. This step I find was very necessary, in as much, as the contractor has failed and provisions are to be furnished by the Qur. Master Genls Dept. Everything, however, will be provided

---

[8] Andrew Jackson Papers, 1st series, Vol. 51–52, microfilm reel 26. Major General Jackson commanded the Southern Division of the army from 1815 until 1821. Heitman, *Historical Register*, I, 566.

93

in time for the troops, who are expected here by the 28th instant. They passed Philadelphia on the 10th.

I calculate, very confidently, on reaching St. Louis with the Regt. by the end of May, where I shall be glad to receive any further instructions you may think proper to give: Those already recd. shall be scrupulously observed.

I will avail myself of the honor of informing you of the time of the embarkation of the Regt. here, of our progress, from convenient points, as we descend the Ohio, and of our arrival at St. Louis.

I beg you to believe that the greatest activity & promptness will be exercised in discharging the duties confided to me, and permit me to express hope, that the whole will be performed in such a manner, as to meet your approbation & views.

7. *Henry Atkinson to Jacob Brown*[9]

PITTSBURGH, PENNSYLVANIA

May 5, 1819

I have the honor to inform you that my Regt. and the detachment of the 5th arrived at this place on the 1st instant at 3 oclock P.M., in good health & fine spirits. We have suffered from desertions, but probably not more than might have been expected, say something *more than forty*. I feel persuaded, however, from many appearances, that the object of our march will be successfully attained, indeed, as far as any exertion on my part will go to justify such an anticipation, I promise as much as my humble capacity will afford.

As I mentioned to you in a former communication, the orders that I have recd. relative to the expedition before me, contain nothing more than you were made acquainted with at Washington, which you gave me the outlines of when I had the pleasure of seeing you at *Albany*.

Our *transport* boats are *not quite ready*. I think, however, we

9 Jacob Brown Papers, Clements Library, University of Michigan.

shall be able to embark by the 8th instant. I shall avail myself of the honor of writing to you again before my departure.

8. Henry Atkinson to John Calhoun[10]

PITTSBURGH, PENNSYLVANIA
May 8, 1819

I have the honor to state to you that the troops are engaged in loading the camp equipage & baggage on board the transports, and that we shall sail about 4 oclock P.M.

9. Henry Atkinson to Andrew Jackson[11]

SIX MILES ABOVE
CINCINATTI, OHIO
May 15, 1819

... Our numbers were small when we moved from Plattsburgh & are rendered less by forty some desertions on the March. I think, however, we shall lose few, if any more.

The troops embarked at Pittsburgh ([as] I informed you they would) on the evening of the [8th inst.]. We have been delayed by head winds & may expe[ct to be] retarded by the same cause between this & the mo[uth of the] River. Nevertheless, as I shall press on with all poss[ible] dispatch, I anticipate reaching St. Louis by the 7th or [8th] the insuing month, perhaps earlier.

10. Andrew Jackson to Henry Atkinson[12]

HEAD QUARTERS
NASHVILLE, TENNESSEE
May 15, 1819

... In addition to the instructions already given for your government I deem it necessary only to recommend the strictest ob-

---

10 Adjutant General, Letters Received, RG 94.

11 Andrew Jackson Papers, 1st series, Vol. 53–54, microfilm reel 27. The manuscript is torn and the bracketed material is my reconstruction of missing or illegible material.

12 Andrew Jackson Papers, 1st series, Vol. L–O, microfilm reel 63.

servance of *caution* and *vigilence* in ascending the Missouri. It may be necessary by acts of friendship to quiet the fears and conciliate the feelings as much as possible, but at the same time to suffer no act or profession, on their part to find you for a moment off your guard. The Treachery of the Indian character will never justify the reposing of confidence in their professions, be always prepared for defence and ready to inflict examplary punishment on the offenders when necessary.

The British Traders will no doubt excite the Indians to hostility. They ought in my opinion to be hung, where ever they are found among the Indian tribes within our Territory a few examples would be sufficient and the Commanding Officer of the Troops is the proper authority to judge of their guilt and Order their execution. But the over cautious policy of the Executive, has directed that they only be arrested and reported to him (as expressed in your orders). This instead of puting down the influence of British (*emmissaries*) I fear, will have a very different effect.

11. Henry Atkinson to Andrew Jackson[13]

MOUTH OF CUMBERLAND RIVER
May 23, 1819

I have the honor to inform you that I have progressed thus far with the 6th Regt & the detachment of the 5th. Unusually strong head winds has delayed us two or three days: We shall, however, if the weather holds good, reach the Mississippi early tomorrow, & St. Louis, probably, in twelve days after.

The troops are in good health. The sick of my own Regt amounts to only eighteen, & the detachment of the 5th to five, and I think I may safely add, that every thing promises a successful issue of the expedition before us.

13 Andrew Jackson Papers, 1st series, Vol. 53–54, microfilm reel 27.

12. *Henry Atkinson to John Calhoun*[14]

ST. LOUIS, MISSOURI
June 7, 1819

I have the honor to inform you that I arrived at this place on the morning of the 1st instant, in the Steam Boat St. Louis. I accompanied the troops from Pittsburgh until we reached the distance of about twenty-five miles up the Mississippi above the mouth of the Ohio, when I left the transports & took passage in the Steam Boat, to facilitate my arrival for the purpose of forwarding the preparations for our ascent up the Missouri.

Two of Col. Johnsons Steam Boats had arrived, a few days before me, with provision; and a third, The Jefferson, was lying 130 miles below, loaded with ordnance & ordnance stores. She had halted in consequence of a part of her Machinery having given way. I understand she is nearly repaired & is expected up in a day or two. The fourth Boat, the Calhoun, is expected to arrive in four or five days.

It will probably take up a fortnight to finish inspecting the provisions intended for the supplies on the Missouri. So soon as this important business is over, I shall take my final departure for the upper Missouri.

In the course of three or four days I shall send off, Colonel Chambers, with two hundred & seventy men of his Reg. from Belle Fontaine, in four of the transport Boats which were brought from Pittsburgh, to join the part of that regiment at Cantonment Martin, with instructions to be ready to ascend with my Reg. on its arrival there with the Steam Boats.

The Rifle Reg. will be transported in Keel Boats & my own in the four Steam Boats attended by four Keel Boats. In accompanying the Steam boats with four Keels, I shall be able to afford the former every assistance they may need to facilitate & insure a speedy voyage. I have not the least doubt of the practicability of

---

[14] United States Army, Quartermaster Department Papers, Library of Congress; 16 Cong., 2 sess., *House Executive Document No. 110*, 159–60.

97

navigating the Missouri with steam power, notwithstanding the almost universal opinion to the contrary.

My Reg. & the detachment of the 5th arrived this morning, & will probably reach Belle Fontaine today. The troops continue in good health, and no unfavorable accident has occurred on their passage, beyond the loss of two men on the Ohio.

I do not think that we can get off sooner than a fortnight. Col. Johnson will most probably not be ready earlier. I think, however, notwithstanding the delay anticipated in the preparation of the Steam Boats, that every thing promises the most favorable issue to the expedition. Yet it is impossible for me to say, before I reach the Council Bluffs, how much of the plan can be executed this season; so much as may be prudent, you may rely on being done, having at the same time due regard to your instructions & views on the subject.

The steam Boat under the care of Maj. Long is a short distance below, & will probably arrive today. I understand she gives every evidence of answering the purposes for which she is intended.

The detachment of the 5th Reg. under Capt. Pelham,[15] is at Belle Fontaine. The part of it intended for the Rifle Reg. will be immediately transferd, & the remainder, with the detachment that accompanyied my regiment, ordered up the Mississippi to join the 5th.

13. Department Orders[16]

St. Louis, Missouri
June 8, 1819

... The Detachment of the Rifle Regt. at Belle Fontaine, will embark for Cantonment Martin under the immediate orders of Col. Chambers, at as early a day as it may be practicable, to prepare it, for the voyage. Four of the Second size transport Boats, of the 6th Regt, are to be selected by Col. Chambers, for the transportation

[15] Captain Peter Pelham, Fifth Infantry. Heitman, *Historical Register*, I, 781.
[16] Ninth Military Department Orders, United States Army Commands, Vol. 93, RG 98; Stephen W. Kearny Papers, Missouri Historical Society.

of the Detachment. Fifty days rations, for the Command, is to be drawn from the Department of the Commissariat, with an allowance of an extra ration of liquor. As much of the clothing of the Rifle Regt, as the transports can carry conveniently, is to be taken to the Regt by the Detachment, besides as much rifle powder (to be drawn from the deposit, at Belle Fontaine) as Col. Chambers may deem requisite for his Regt. On the arrival of the Detachment at Cantonment Martin, Col. Chambers will immediately reorganize his Regt, to place it on the most efficient footing, that the number & character of the force may afford, & have it in readiness to join the 6th Regt. on its arrival at that point, and to accompany it up the Missouri. . . .

In closing this order, the Col. Comd avails himself of the occasion to express his entire satisfaction, of the conduct of the 6th Regt during its long & fatiguing march from Plattsburg. The facility with which it has moved, has exceeded the expectations of the Department of War, & of the Comd Genl. & will form a bright ora in the character of the Corps. But altho so much has been done, there still remains, further duty, to close the march. The Council Bluffs, are yet to be reached, & every officer & man must be ready to move, at a short notice, to accomplish the object. The Regt. will be transported in Steam Boats, to that point, where permanent arrangements, will be made, for its accomadation. The Council Bluffs are situated in the finest climate, & district of the Country in America & may be justly esteemed, the most desirable post, on the Continent.

Requisitions, for one years clothing are to be immediately made out, by the 6th Regt & rendered by the Regimental Quarter Master to Col. Clemson,[17] at St. Louis, who will deliver upon them, forthwith—A Requisition for Eight hundred pair of shoes, & an extra suit of fatigue clothing for each man of the Regt, will be made in addition, by the Qr. Mr. for the extra issues during the Summer & Autumn.

[17] Lieutenant Colonel Eli B. Clemson, assistant commissary of issues. Heitmen, *Historical Register*, I, 309.

14. *Henry Atkinson to John Calhoun*[18]

ST. LOUIS, MISSOURI
June 19, 1819

I am sorry to inform you that Col. Johnsons steam Boats have not all arrived. The Jefferson came up last night and brought our ordnance and ordnance stores. The Calhoun is still behind and has not been heard of. I have determined however, not to wait for her and intend to proceed in six or seven days with the three steam Boats & four of our Keels. The troops are ready to move, but it will probably require, several days to reload the steam Boats.

The full quantity of provisions that Col. Johnson was to furnish, has not come to hand; all that has yet come, is six months supply for the 5th Regiment (already sent up the river) & five months salted meat, three months flour & a proportion of small rations now ready for the upper Missouri. Colonel Johnson, expects an ample supply daily, but should he be disappointed and the provisions not arrive by the time we are ready, to move, I shall have six months supply, completed by the commissary, by purchases that can be made here on reasonable terms—very large quantities of flour can be had at, from, seven to eight dollars per Barrel. Indeed I am well convinced that the Troops may be supplied on the upper Missouri on reasonable terms should Col. Johnson, not comply with his engagements, a circumstance that I do not apprehend. As I shall be better able to give you a decisive account respecting the manner in which we are to be supplied (beyond what is already received) in a few days, I will close this communication by assuring you that I see no obstacle (altho' there are some that I did not anticipate) that will prevent my carrying your views of the expedition into good effect.

I shall certainly establish myself at the Council Bluffs, this season & verry possibly carry the Rifle Regiment to the Mandan village; the latter however must depend on circumstances, that

[18] U.S. Army, Quartermaster Department Papers, Library of Congress; 16 Cong., 2 sess., *House Executive Document No. 110*, 160–61.

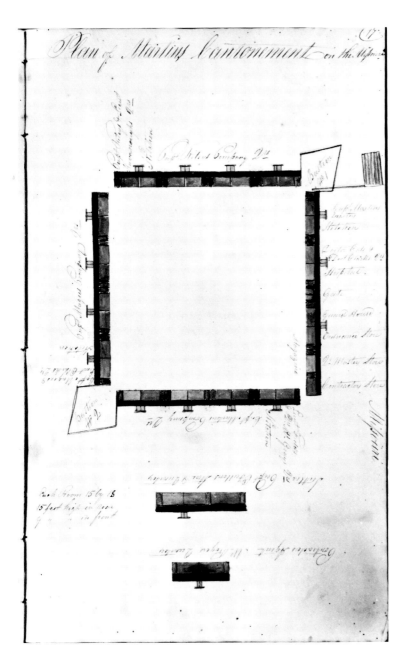

Sketch of Martin's Cantonment (1818–19) from the journal

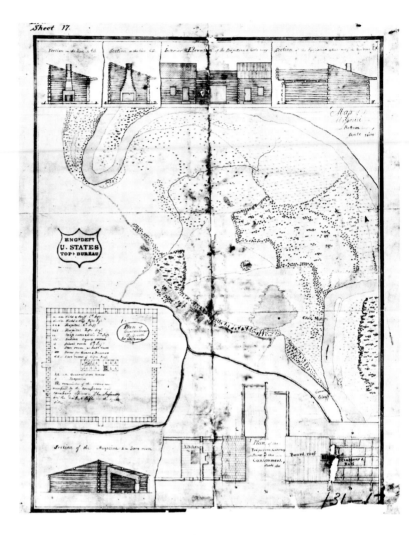

Map of the Missouri Bottom, 1820

cannot be foreseen. I shall not risk too much nor will I leave any thing undone that I may think can be prudently accomplished.

The exploring steam Boat is still here; Maj. Long, I understand intends, departing for the upper country tomorrow. All the assistance he may want shall be promptly offered.

15. Thomas Jesup to Trueman Cross[19]

ST. LOUIS, MISSOURI
June 25, 1819

I have recd your letters dated the 19th and 26th of May, and am equally astonished at the amount drawn for by the Johnsons and their silence on the subject. I fortunately made provisional arrangements for the expedition soon after my arrival in the western country. Had I depended on Coll Johnson we must have failed. He has three steam-boats, but they are not yet in readiness to move and the provisions which should have been delivered at least a month ago, have not arrived.

Colo Chambers with a large detachment of riflemen moved about twelve days ago, in boats furnished by my department, and Capt. McGunnigle is making arrangements today to forward a considerable quantity of clothing and ordnance stores in the same way.

The Johnsons are entirely without Military Capacity—indeed! if it were possible to consolidate the talents and energies of the whole concern and infuse them thus consolidated into one individual, there would hardly be sufficient for a common Quarter Master Sergeant.

If stupid newspaper paragraphs, which in my estimation are as degrading to their authors as they are insulting to the good sence of the community, were sufficient to accomplish the objects of the government, Colo J and his associates would be able indeed —but it will be found that something more than idle professions and ostentatious boastings will be necessary to insure success.

[19] Secretary of War, Letters Received, Registered Series, RG 107.

I wish you to prevent the acceptance or payment of any further drafts of Colo Johnson or of his brother, on account of the Quarter Masters Department, unless they be approbated by Captain Pickett,[20] Capt. McGunnegle or myself.

The whole expence of the expedition, including the transportation of provisions would not have exceeded ninety thousand dollars had our arrangements been made independent of the Johnsons. Ten steam-boats if required could have been employed at Cincinnati, Louisville and St. Louis, and at about one-half the amount per ton which Colo Johnson expects to receive.

The 6th regiment will move in two or three days. I shall probably accompany it two or three hundred miles.

16. Henry Atkinson to John Calhoun[21]

ST. CHARLES, MISSOURI
July 11, 1819

I have delayed writing for a few days, that I might be enabled to give such an account of our progress, as would present a data by which you could judge how much of the plan of the expedition can be effected this season.

In explanation of the delay that will seem to have taken place in the sailing of the troops from Belle Fontaine for the upper Missouri, I beg leave to state, that after exerting myself for more than a month, I was not able 'till the 2d inst to get from Col. Johnson, the Contractor, a sufficient quantity of provisions to justify the movement, and then, only five months supply, and of that quantity, about eight hundred barrels of flour were purchased in St. Louis a few days before, on my stating to Col. Johnson, [that] if it was not immediately furnished, I would order the purchase to be made on acco[unt] of the U States. Vinigar, Pease & Beans are deficient in the above supply, & salt has been furnished by the Commissary.

20 Captain James C. Picket, acting deputy Quartermaster General. Heitman, *Historical Register*, I, 790.

21 U.S. Army, Quartermaster Department Papers, Library of Congress; 16 Cong., 2 sess., *House Executive Document No. 110*, 161–62.

Immediately on the receipt of the provisions, I ordered the Troops (the 6th Reg.) to embark, four Companies in Keel Boats, & four on board the three steam Boats. They sailed on the 4th and 5th inst. The Keel Boats make fine progress & are probably some seventy or eighty miles up the River by this time. Two of the steam Boats went a ground on the day they sailed & were with much difficulty got off. T[h]ey all reached this by evening of the 8th inst. On the 9th the Johnson & Expedition proceeded on. The Jefferson followed the next day & after going three miles came to, [stopped] in consequence of having broken part of her machinery; the Engineer is now repa[ir]ing it, & she is expected to sail in the morning. I have strong hopes the two first vessels will succeed in reaching Cant Martin & the Council Bluffs, but I am doubtful of the success of the latter. Should either, or all of the steam Boats fail, arrangements are & will be made in the Qur Master Gens department to take up their cargoes in good season.

The delays have proceeded from causes beyond my controul, but you may rest satisfied that I will establish myself at the Council Bluffs this season.

The most ample aid has been on all occassions given by the Qur Master Genl dept, and I regret that any thing relating to transportation connected with the expedition has been delegated to other hands.

Colonel Johnson has recd large supplies of provisions since the troops sailed, but not enough I am convinced to fulfill his contracts. I have ordered the Commissary to have it shipped as fast as it [is] inspected, & push it on after us. Should there be any deficiency in the quantity, I have no doubt the Commissary will be able to meet it by purchases in the Boonslick settlements.

I have paid every attention to forwarding the ordnance, Munitions of war, Hospital stores & clothing for the Mississippi, all of which proceeded a few days ago under charge of a detachment of the 5th Reg. which were at Belle Fontaine, & which I had detained for the purpose.

I proceed tomorrow on horseback up the river, in order that I may be able more readily to supply any deficiency that may occur in transportation by the failure of any of the steam boats. . . .

17. Henry Atkinson to John Calhoun[22]

FRANKLIN, MISSOURI
July 30, 1819

I have the honor to inform you that four companies of the 6th Regiment in Keel Boats and a detachment of a company and a half in the Steam Boat, Expedition, arrived here on the 22d instant. The Troops in the Keels proceeded up the river after waiting a day to dry their baggage. The Expedition has been detained 'till this morning to repair her machinery. She will probably reach Martin Cantonment in twelve days. The other two Steam Boats were sixty miles below this, two days ago. It is possible they may be up tomorrow.

We have been verry much retarded in our progress by accidents happening to the Steam Boats and it is somewhat doubtful whether we shall be able to get them up finally, should they, however, fail the Keels which are behind with the residue of the provisions will warrant a supply both of rations & transportation, to ensure our makeing the counsil Bluffs in good season. We have received from Col. Johnson nearly the quantity of provisions which I required for the use of the Troops for the present year, statement of which shall be forwarded as soon as one is received from the commissary.

The last of the supplies were shipped and put under way after us on the 22d instant.

I wait only for the Steam Boat Johnson when I shall set out to join the Troops above. Permit me to repeat, that you may confidently rely on my establishing myself at the Council Bluffs this season.

22 U.S. Army, Quartermaster Department Papers, Library of Congress; 16 Cong., 2 sess., *House Executive Document No. 110*, 163.

18. Henry Atkinson to John Calhoun[23]

FRANKLIN, MISSOURI
August 13, 1819

I had the honor on the 30th ultimo to advise you of the situation of the troops destined for the upper Missouri & of the transport vessels attached to the expedition. Col. Chambers is now with a detachment of his Regt. & four Companies of the 6th Regt. at Fort Osage. The Steam Boat Expedition with a Company & a half was progressing three days ago about fifty miles below Fort Osage. The Johnson with a Company was also progressing forty-five miles above this place the day before yesterday. I was advised by express two days ago that the Jefferson with a Company & a half on board, was a ground forty miles below. The Captain of the Boat had notified the commanding officer of the troops on board that he could proceed no further. Agreeably to special instructions left the commanding officer of the detachment an express was sent by him early on the day of the failure of the Boat to St. Louis for Keel boats to receive her cargo. The express would reach there in two days, and as the Asst. Depy. Qur. Master Genl. was ordered to hold Keel boats in readiness to meet any failure of the Steam Boats, they will no doubt be under way in two, or three days. A Keel Boat was sent to the Jefferson from this place yesterday to receive from her such articles as may be wanted above for immediate use.

Four Keel Boats with more than eight hundred barrels of provisions & the clothing of both Regiments must by this time be at, or near Fort Osage; on their arrival Col. Chambers will proceed with the troops at that place for Cantonment Martin.

Having arranged every thing necessary to ensure the arrival of the Jefferson's cargo at an early day above, I shall set out today to join the Johnson at Fort Osage, & from thence proceed in her to the Cantonment above.

Should the Expedition & Johnson both fail, an occurrence I do

[23] U.S. Army, Quartermaster Department Papers, Library of Congress; 16 Cong., 2 sess., *House Executive Document No. 110*, 163–65.

not much apprehend, my arrangements will enable me to get their cargoes taken up in good season.

I expect to move from Martin Cantonment for the Council Bluffs by the 10th Sepr, and as the distance is only two hundred & fifty miles, we ought to expect to make it by the first of October, a day early enough to commence Hutting for the winter.

The tardiness of the Jefferson would have authorized me to have discharged her two or three weeks ago, which would have been so much time saved. But, knowing as I did, that Col. Johnson had drawn largely on acct of transportation, I thought it most prudent, as I had yet time on my hands, to wait 'till a failure was acknowledged on the part of the Boat, that He might not have the slightest reason to say that any interference on the part of the Comg officer of the expedition caused to him a loss. Indeed I have been particularly careful to avoid giving the smalest clue by which He could claim indemnity from government for losses which he must certainly sustain in his contract for transportation.

When I wrote on the 30th ultimo, I was induced to believe from information recd from the commissary at St. Louis, that Col. Johnson had nearly finished to complete the 400,000 rations which I required for the troops on this river. But from a recent letter recd from the same officer, there is a deficiency. The quantity recd. is, 356,608 rations of meat, 324,648 do. of flour, 5,550 do. of corn meal, 5,836 gallons of whiskey, 6,664 lbs. candels & 9,083 lbs of soap. From this statement, Sir, you may see how entirely Col. Johnson has failed in this part of his contract.

When I left St. Louis He had not sent more than 100,000 rations up the Mississippi. I much fear his failure in that quarter will be in greater proportion than it is in this.

19. Henry Atkinson to John Calhoun[24]

CHARITON, MISSOURI
August 14, 1819

In the several communications which I have had the honor to

24 U.S. Army, Quartermaster Department Papers, Library of Congress; 16 Cong., 2 sess., *House Executive Document No. 110*, 165–66.

make you, I have only adverted to the progress of the expedition up the Missouri. As the part of the plan of the expedition which is contemplated to be effected the next season will carry a part of the forces to a distant & remote point, I beg leave to suggest to you the propriety of directing that the supplies for the troops be ready for shipment at some point on the Missouri as early as the first day of March.

Provisions for the troops, stationed in this section of the country, have been heretofore drawn from Kentucky. But as the meat part of the ration can be abundantly & cheaply supplied in the neighbourhood of Franklin & this place, it will be certainly preferable to have the necessary supply engaged in these places. If the commissary was instructed to purchase, fine pork could be had at three & a half dollars p hundred & beef at about the same price, and as the country abounds in salt, it might be barrel'd up at a small expense. If it should be thought more advisable to purchase it in a cured state, a sufficient quantity can be engaged at twelve dollars p barrel. Bread stuff can also be procured in the same section of country, but probably not altogether of flour. Kiln-dried corn meal can be obtained to any extent, which might probably answer a good purpose. The advantages arising from the purchases being made in this part of the country would be two fold. The saving of transportation from Kentucky & the advanced position of the provisions towards their ultimate point of destination, thereby ensuring their early movement up the river.

With respect to the proper mode of transportation up the Missouri (which ought never to be taken out of the hands of the Qur Master Generals department) I have no hesitation in saying that Keel boats is preferable to any other. Their progress, altho' slow, can be calculated upon with certainty. Their average distance p day may be estimated at fifteen miles. Hence, if they were to commence their voyage as early as the first of March, it would be reasonable to calculate on their reaching the Mandan Village by the middle of July, allowing twenty-five or thirty days for casualties & other delays.

The failure of Col. Johnson to fulfill his contract for supplies this year, I presume will preclude his being depended upon to furnish for the next. Indeed I should feel apprehensive of not being able to accomplish the object which you have in view, were I made to depend on such a source. In making this observation, I do not wish to be understood as impeaching the integrity of Col. Johnson, but I deem it a sound maxim not to trust the man who has once disappointed you.

I shall proceed today to Fort Osage to join the Johnson, from whence I shall take passage in her for Martin Cantonment, and calculate on reaching the Council Bluffs by the first of October. After establishing the troops at that, or some eligible place in its vicinity, and arranging every thing necessary for their security & comfort, I shall return to St. Louis to superintend the arrangements for the next season.

20. John Calhoun to Henry Atkinson[25]

DEPARTMENT OF WAR
August 18, 1819

While in South Carolina and on my return to Washington I received your several communications under dates of 8th & 17th of April, 4th of May and 7th of June, and within a few days that of the 11th of July.

The belief that your movement up the Missouri would commence before an answer could reach you, with the necessity of laying that part of your communication which related to the Indian Agent and Indian affairs before the President, prevented my immediate reply.

On the return of the President they were submitted to him for his orders, and by his direction, Mr. [Benjamin] O'Fallon the Indian Agent has been instructed to consult and report his proceedings to you as the Commander of the Department, on all subjects connected with his duties as an Agent. I have no doubt

25 Secretary of War, Letters Sent, Military Affairs, RG 107.

but that you will find your anticipation as to his abilities and character correct. He was very well recommended and on a short personal acquaintance I am favorable impressed towards him.

The President also directs that you will, whenever you think the publick interest will be promoted, hold treaties of friendship with the tribes without our limits, in which treaties you may establish such general rules for the intercourse between them and those under your command and such of our traders or Citizens, who may visit them, as you may judge expedient. You may also treat for sites of forts with a sufficient tract of Country around, not exceeding fifteen miles square, as you may judge advisable. It would be a proper mark of respect for the Agent and would probably be attended with good effects, if you were to associate him with you in the negociations when it can conveniently be done.

To bind the Indians to our interest, to impress them with a high idea of our power and justice in order to [promote] the protection of our frontier and the extension of our trade, are among the important objects of the expedition; and entire confidence is reposed that you will seize every opportunity to effect them.

The delay which took place in the movement of the expedition is to be regretted, but to yourself and the Quarter Master General no blame can attach, as it appears to have arisen wholly out of the arrangement of the contractor. It affords me much pleasure to say that all your movements have indicated a promptitude and soundness of judgement which have increased the previously favorable impression of the Department. It is not probable that you will proceed beyond Council Bluff this season. It is much more important to proceed securely, than rapidly; but how far they may be combined you can best judge. Whatever position you may take you will render as secure as practicable. You will let no opportunity pass without keeping the Department fully informed of your movements and to furnish all such information as may enable it to judge of the probable success of the Expedition.

21. Henry Atkinson to John Calhoun[26]

FORT OSAGE, MISSOURI
August 25, 1819

I have the honor to inform you that I arrived at this post on the 23d inst. The detachment of the Rifle Regt. & five Companies of the 6th moved on the same day under the comd. of Col. Chambers, in Keel Boats & the Steam Boat Expedition, for Martin Cantonment.

I left the Johnson on the 22d at the Miami Bottom eighty miles below. As she had passed the great obstructions near the Grand River, she may be reasonably expected to reach this by tomorrow evening. I shall set out from this place the day after tomorrow, to meet the troops, two days following, at Martin Cantonment, from whence we shall depart for the Council Bluffs, at farthest, by the 8th or 10th proximo, and our arrival there can not be protracted longer than the end of the month. The cargo of the Jefferson is by this time reshipped in Keels, & will, agreeably to instructions, follow on, escorted by a detachment of the 6th Regt. under under [sic] Capt. Bliss.

From information obtained here, & from traders from above, I have every reason to believe that the several Indian tribes in this section of the country will continue on friendly & peaceable terms with the United States. Hostilities however, still exist among themselves. Indeed, there is scarcely a tribe, but what is at war with some one or more tribes. These wars consist of excursions made by small parties of one nation against another, and amount to the loss of but few lives & the stealing of a few horses.

22. Department Orders[27]

MARTIN CANTONMENT
September 4, 1819

At daybreak each morning, at the beating of Reveille, every

[26] U.S. Army, Quartermaster Department Papers, Library of Congress; 16 Cong., 2 sess., *House Executive Document No. 110*, 166–67.
[27] Ninth Military Department Orders, Vol. 93, RG 98.

preparation, will be made to embark. Half an hour after Reveille, a Rocket will be fired from the Transport of the comg officer, & every Boat must be put in motion. A distance of from 50 to 100 yards, will be preserved between each of the boats, while in motion. This distance must be preserved with all possible exactness. At 8 o'clock, a swivel will be fired, as a signal for Breakfast. At this signal, the Boats will close to within 50 yds of each other, & then halt for Breakfast. At 9 o'clock the Bugle will sound & the Boats be again put in motion. At 12 o'clock a swivel will fire, as a signal for dinner; the Boats will again close up within 50 paces of each other & halt to dine. At one o'clock the Flotilla will again be put in motion, at the sound of a bugle. At an hour before sundown a swivel will fire as a signal to halt for the night. The Rifle Flankers, must be called in & the Boats approach within 20 paces of each other; disembark, & each Boats crew encamp on the ground opposite to their Boats, upon the margin of the river paralel to it. The Companies on the Right & Left Flank will form at Right angles with the river with one of their Flanks resting on it & facing from the encampment. Previous to dark the men must be formed in single rank, in front of their Camp their arms inspected and they instructed that in case of Alarm that is to be their position until further orders.

Two picket Guards of a Sgt., Cpl. & nine men each will be posted 80 paces in front of the main camp & a Cpl. and three men will be placed as a Guard the same distance in front of the Companies on the right and left flank. In the event of discovering suspicious Indians while the Flotilla is in motion, it will be announced by two swivels which must be considered as an order to prepare for action & close towards the Comd officer to receive his orders. In case of an actual attack upon the centre or rear of the column, a swivel will be discharged from every Boat & each Boat will repair as near as possible to the scene of action & the senior officer present will make the most advantageious disposition of the Troops until the arrival of the Commdg Officer. A signal of distress will be four guns fired in quick succession. It will be repeated by every boat. The Front will halt, the nearest boat approach & render every possible assistance. When an accident occurs which can be repaired within the boat, without assistance, a signal of distress will not be fired.

23. *Department Orders*[28]

MARTIN CANTONMENT
September 5, 1819

The troops will embark to day, at 1 o'clock. At half after 12 the General, will be beat, by the drums of the 6th Infy. The tents are to be struck, & the embarkation commence. The movement of the boats will be indicated by the established signals . . . .

24. *Henry Atkinson to John Calhoun*[29]

MARTIN CANTONMENT
September 6, 1819

I have the honor to inform you that I arrived at this post on the 31st ultimo. The detachment of Riflemen under Col. Chambers & five Companies of the 6th Regt got up two days previous, accompanied by the Steam Boat Expedition.

The Steam Boat Johnson is yet behind, but may be expected up in a day or two. The [s.b.] Expedition has halted here, it being deemed impracticable, in consequence of the lowness of the River, to get her to the Council Bluffs. The Johnson will, probably, be able to reach that point as her draught of water is much lighter. The cargo of the Expedition has been reshipped in our transport boats & a Keel employed by Col. Johnson's agent, and should the Johnson fail I have ample means within my controul to have her cargo taken up in good season.

The Rifle Reg & five Companies of the 6th embark today at

---

28 *Ibid.*

29 U.S. Army, Quartermaster Department Papers, Library of Congress; 16 Cong., 2 sess., *House Executive Document No. 110*, 167–68.

one o'clock for the Council Bluffs.[30] We shall, no doubt, make the march in twenty days.

The Infantry which were on board of the Steam Boat Jefferson are charged with the safe conduct of the Keels that recd her cargo, & may be expected to join us above by the 15th proximo. Those on board of the Johnson will be up sooner. Therefore, it may be safely calculated that the principle part of the troops will be established at the Council Bluffs, by the first of October & the residue by the 20th, together, with all our ordinance, munitions & provisions for twelve months.

I take the liberty of enclosing a communication from Maj. Biddle respecting the conduct of a party of the Pawnee Tribe of Indians toward himself & party, whilst on a tour through the Kansas Country.[31] In consequence of the transaction I have requested Maj. O'Fallon, Indian Agent, to inhibit all trade with the tribes till proper restitution is made, which, I have no doubt, will be promptly done.

P.S. our delays must be attributed to the tardy movement of the Steam Boats alone.

25. *Department Orders*[32]

CAMP ON MISSOURI

September 24, 1819

Discharging of Fire arms, either in Camp or within four hundred yards of the lines, or from the Flotilla except by special permission by the Act. Asst. Insp. Gen. or in obedience to the established signals, is in future positively prohibited.

The unfortunate occurrence of today, in the death of one of the Riflemen, is a melancholy instance of the necessity of a rigid compliance with this regulation; and it is expected that every

30 This letter is dated incorrectly. It was written on September 5. The sailing orders for the flotilla (item # 23 above) are dated September 5. The journal entry for September 5 also gives that as the day the troops left for Council Bluffs.

31 On August 24, 1819, a war party of Pawnee braves robbed a detachment of Major Long's group of their horses and some equipment. Thwaites, *James Account*, I, 203–205.

32 Ninth Military Department Orders, Vol. 93, RG 98.

officer will not only promptly enforce it in his command, but that he will also implicitly obey it himself.

26. *Henry Atkinson to Andrew Jackson*[33]

CAMP MISSOURI
October 3, 1819

I avail myself of the earliest opporty. to inform you of my arrival with the Rifle Regt & five & a half companies of the 6th at a point a few miles below this early on the morning of the 29th ultimo., where we remained till yesterday morning to examine the neighbouring country for the purpose of selecting a position to canton the troops. Having fixed on this place, (an extensive rich bottom, covered with timber suitable for huts, situated a mile above the Council Bluffs) we reached it yesterday evening. Tomorrow we shall commence huting, & probably cover ourselves in five weeks.

Light Company A & a part of B had left the Steam Boat *Jefferson* in keels & were on the 7th ultimo eighty miles below Fort Osage. They may be expected to reach this by the 20th inst. together with the cargo of the *Jefferson*, escorted by Capt. Bliss' command. Battalion Company H is also behind, it was on board of the *Johnson* who broke part of her machinery thirty miles above fort Osage. Keel Boats were discharged here some days ago & went down to her; therefore, the cargo & the company will, no doubt, be up in all this month.

As the means of conveying this letter is some what precarious, I defer giving a detailed account 'till some few days hence, when I expect a light boat will return to St. Louis.

27. *Henry Atkinson to John Calhoun*[34]

CAMP MISSOURI
October 19, 1819

I have the honor to acknowledge the receipt of your communi-

---

33 Andrew Jackson Papers, 1st series, Vol. 54, microfilm reel 27.

34 U.S. Army, Quartermaster Department Papers, Library of Congress; 16 Cong., 2 sess., *House Executive Document No. 110,* 169–71.

cation of the 18th August. It gives me great satisfaction to learn
that my movements up to the 11th July have met your approbation; since then many difficulties have occurred. The three steam
Boats, as you have already been informed, all failed. One below
Franklin, another near the mouth of the Kansas river in the
wilderness, & the third at Cantonment Martin. These difficulties
have all been surmounted. One of the Keel boats with troops &
provisions from the Jefferson reached here on the 12th inst, an
other is near at hand; a third may be expected in four days & the
fourth about the same time. The Expeditions cargo has been
bro't up & the boats sent to the Johnson for hers, should arrive by
the end of the month, by which time I have but little doubt, from
the information given by Capt. Bliss, who lately came up in a
Keel from the Jefferson, that all the boats with supplies will reach
here, with the exception of one that left Belle Fontaine on the
15th of Septr freighted with flour, vinigar, &c.

If the provisions which have been shipped reach us in safety, of
which there is but little doubt, we shall have a sufficient supply
of flour & most of the small parts of the ration. To provide against
a defficiency of meat, an article the contractor fell far short in, I
caused beef cattle to be contracted for & driven to this place. Up-
wards of two hundred head have arrived, which will make our
supply ample.

We have progressed with our barracks as high as the roof,
which will soon be put on. Boards for covering, floors &c. are in a
state of forwardness, & I think every thing promises fair to warrant a belief, that the troops will be comfortably quartered in all
next month.

The Barrack are laid out, as well for defence, as for accomoda-
tion. They form a square, each curtain presenting a front of 520
feet, made of heavy logs & the walls about sixteen feet high & the
whole of the roofs sloping to the interior. In the centre of each
curtain there is a projection of twenty feet, its width twenty with
a heavy ten foot gate in the front. These projections will be

pierced with three embrasures for cannon, two raking the curtain each way from the centre & the other through the gate to the front. The upper part of the projection will have a second floor & will project over the tower part to afford loops to fire down through. It will be raised to a barbet[35] height & will answer for cannon and musketry. The Barrack rooms, the exterior of which form the curtains, are 20 feet by 20 & will be pierced with loop holes for small arms. When completed, no force will be able to carry the work without the aid of cannon. As soon as the Engineer, Lt. Talcott, arrives, who took passage in the Johnson, you shall be furnished with a plan of the work & a topographical survey of the ground, the river, and the adjacent country.

I am led to believe from Hardhart, an [Iowa] Indian chief, who has often traversed the country, that an excellent road may be made with but little trouble, from hence on the north side of the river across to Chariton, & embrace only a distance of 180 to 200 miles.

Deeming such a communication with the interior of the first importance on many accounts, I shall send an oficer in the course of four or five days with a party of some six or eight soldiers to mark out a road by the nearest route over the country alluded to. The party will be supplied with pack horses, & the Ioway chief, Hardhart, as a guide. The officer will take with him proper instruments and be instructed to make a topographical sketch of the country. As soon as the road is marked out, the route will afford an easy communication between the post & the post office at Chariton which may be kept up once a month, and oftener if necessary, by expresses, & which will be put in practice . . . .

The troops, notwithstanding the excessive fatigue to which they have been subjected, enjoy excellent health, & all hands seem well disposed to do their duty . . . .

---

35 A barbette is a specially protected platform on which guns are mounted to fire over a parapet. *Webster's Dictionary*, 175.

"Pawnee Council" by Samuel Seymour

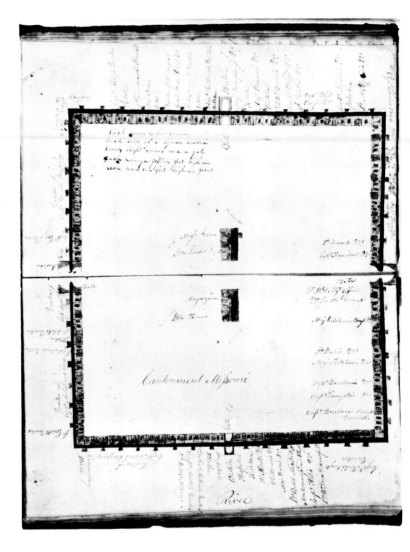

Sketch of Cantonment Missouri (1819–20) from the journal

28. Department Orders[36]

CANTONMENT MISSOURI
November 2, 1819

A mily post is established at this place & it is to be called & officially known as soon as the Barracks are erected, by the name of Cantonment Missouri.

29. Henry Atkinson to Andrew Jackson[37]

ST. LOUIS, MISSOURI
November 23, 1819

I have the honor to inform you of my return to this place from the Council Bluffs yesterday, after a voyage of twenty days . . . .

The position selected for cantoning the troops lies some thing more than a mile above the Council Bluffs, in a rich bottom on the margin of the river. Many considerations gave to this site a preference over any in the neighborhood. It afforded on the spot & near at hand an abundant supply of timber for huts & fuel, command of the river, an easy access to it for water for general purposes, & a good landing for boats.

The Council Bluffs which have been so highly recommended by Louis & Clark, and others, who have given an account of the country, afford none of the advantages, in a military point of view, that they have been represented to possess. The Bluff is an abrupt elevation of 150 feet with its base washed by the river. Its' summit presents a naked plane runing parrellel with the river near a mile & extending back some seven or eight hundred yards, when it reaches the foot of a second elevation that gradually rises 150 to 160 feet, overlooking & commanding the whole plane below. Added to this objection are many others, such as the trouble & difficulty of getting up timber for buildings & fuel (there being no wood only in the bottom below) no water but that to be

---

[36] Ninth Military Department Orders, Vol. 93, RG 98.
[37] Andrew Jackson Papers, 1st series, Vol. 55–56, microfilm reel 28.

brought up from the river & the position so exposed to the bleak winds, as to deny, almost, existence during the cold season.

Altho' the season was advanced, the abundance, convenience & quality of the timber near the scite we occupy, suggested the propriety of giving to our buildings in their construction a permanent & defensible character, which I think they possess in an eminent degree. . . .[38]

The buildings were not completed on the 2nd inst when I left the Cantonment, but it was generally thought they would be in fifteen days from that time—Nor had Lt. Hailes Compy of the 6 Regt arrived. We met it on the 5th with the steam Boat Johnson's cargo in two keels, sixty miles below the Platte. They no doubt got up in seven or eight days after. Their arrival concentrates the whole force of the Missouri Expedition & adds to our supply of provisions, some 250 barrels, making a quantity sufficient to last till the end of June . . . .

A position near the Council Bluffs seems, in my opinion, of more importance & better calculated to control a more numerous body of Indians than any other on the river. I have, therefore, subject to your approbation concluded to fix one of the permanent posts at the point we occupy . . . .

30. John Gale to Matthew Magee[39]

CANTONMENT MISSOURI
January 23, 1820

[61] A neglected Camp naturally becomes foul and pestilential, soon abounds in uncleaness and corruption, and from a continued accumulation of impurity gradually becomes a nursery of disease. Domestic infection engendered and reared by bad management is readily insinuated into the human system spreads

---

38 The deleted material here repeats the description of the fortifications given in Atkinson's letter to John Calhoun of October 19, 1819 (see Appendix, item # 27).

39 Journal of the Advance Corps of the Military Branch of the Yellowstone Expedition, 61 (hereafter Expedition Journal). Coe Collection, Yale University Library.

like fire and consumes as a conflagration. We should therefore guard against it by every precaution.

It has been allowed by all ages from the time of Moses who commanded the Isrealitish Army to our more enlightened and accomplished Generals of modern date, that human excrement when exposed in the open air may be enumerated among the most obvious causes which contribute to induce putrid diseases.

To prevent the daily augmentation of excrementilous matter around the Cantonment I would respectfully advise the construction of suitable vaults with such instruments as will compel the men to the use of them.

31. John Gale & Thomas Mower to Willoughby Morgan[40]

CANTONMENT MISSOURI
February 5, 1820

[65–66] In compliance with your order, we have the honour to remark that a scorbutic habit[41] has assumed a Distinguished rank among the numerous diseases that afflict our camp. Independent of its own baneful influence on the human system it aggravates and renders more inverterate, all the other diseases to which its unhappy victim is liable.

It should, therefore, be guarded against with the utmost precaution. Every preventive that art can suggest or experience dictate should be used to put a period to its prevalence, and ameliorate its influence. It is a disease occurring after subsisting on putrescent salted animal food with a deficiency of vegetable matter. Excessive fatigue, Indolence, cold and moisture and personal uncleanliness may also be enumerated among its many existing causes.

It is necessary that the men be compelled to air their bedding frequently, and change their flannel and other apparel often, washing the hands, face and feet, and even the whole bodies previous to retiring to bed, frequently in tepid water, wiping dry

40 Expedition Journal, 65–66.
41 This refers to the disease scurvy.

with a course cloth will be very serviceable. The rooms should be perfectly clean with a free admission of air guarding against cold and moisture with sufficient fires.

Salted provisions should be issued as seldom as possible, but fresh meat and such farinaceous substances as can be procured, be substituted.

Vinegar, that invaluable part of the ration, has from necessity been withheld. Too much exertion cannot be used to remedy this deficiency. The salt meat lately issued has been very putricient and under present circumstances, highly deleterious. By deserting it of its external impurities, boiling it in changes of water with the addition of charcoal, it becomes much more wholesome and palatable.

32. John Gale to Willoughby Morgan[42]

CANTONMENT MISSOURI
February 16, 1820

[62-63] I have the honor to acknowledge the receipt of your letter, and would suitable answer it.

The most prevalent disease, at present, among our men is scurvy:

. . . The victim of this dreadful malady is characterised by his extreme feebleness and debility, his pale and bloated complexion; his spongy black and ulcerated gums; by his loosened teeth his foited[43] urine and offensive breath; by the oedematous swelling[44] of his legs; the livid spots on his skin and the universal discolouration of the limbs; by his stiff and swollen joints; his rigid and contracted tendons; his loss of locomotion and by wandering excruciating pains.

Among the whole catalogue of diseases which flesh adhere to none perhaps is more disgusting and loathsome; none tends more

42 Expedition Journal, 62–63.
43 This is the nineteenth-century spelling of fetid.
44 This is the nineteenth-century spelling of edematous. It refers to watery swelling caused by excess body fluid, often called dropsy.

directly to dissolution or more securely marks its victim. Nature unassisted by arts soon yields the miserable subject to the power of this detested and distructive tyrant.

It is necessary in addition to what has been previously recommended in order to stop its further progress and relieve those already under its influence, that the men take only moderate exercise, breathe a pure temporate and dry atmosphere, and use a genirous nutritive diet of fresh animal and vegetable food.

After observing the enlightened liberal and judicious arrangements of the Commandants already adopted in favor of the sick under the most unfavorable circumstances it would perhaps be presumption in the subscriber to make any further suggestions.

33. John Gale to Matthew Magee[45]

CANTONMENT MISSOURI
February 23, 1820

[64] For the purpose of rendering more cheerfull the gloomy appearance of the rooms and for the free admission of air which I deem essentially necessary to the preservation of health, I would respectfully suggest the propriety of opening the windows through the rear of the Barracks and of cutting out the sepperations between the rooms in such a manner that two rooms shall form but one. At present the rooms are small crowded and heated to excess by the intense fires requisite for cooking.

34. John Gale to Board of Officers[46]

CANTONMENT MISSOURI
February 25, 1820

[66–67] I have the honor to submit the following answers to the important questions proposed.

The remote cause of the malady so fatal to our soldiers appears

45 Expedition Journal, 64.
46 Expedition Journal, 66–67. For the membership of this board see the February 26, 1820, entry in the journal.

to have proceeded from the excessive fatigues to which they were necessarily subjected in Navigating the Missouri. Exposure produced numerous diseases, which, from our peculiar situation, were protracted until extreme debility was induced. This debility in concurrence with poor diet, consisting of putrescent salted meat, damaged flour, a deficiency of vegetable matter and groceries, has been and is probably the immediate exciting cause of the complaints from the consequences of which we have much to apprehend.

The variableness of the weather, the alternate humidity and coldness of the atmosphere, the labour requisite in the construction of the Barracks and in producing fuel, may, under existing circumstances have had also an agency in its excitement . . . .

Serious objections may be made, to our local situation; it is flat and low, moist and clayey and in the neighbourhood of a Stagnant pond. Dry, Sandy Elevated places are most conducive to health. Objections may also rest against the regimen of our Troops. They are confined in diet entirely to salted Beef or Bacon of a bad quality, which daily becomes worse; and flour much damaged, without either vegetables, vinegar, or groceries of any description. There are in the Rifle Regiment at present One hundred and twenty seven men sick, more than one hundred of whom are afflicted with scurvey and far from a state of convalescance. Nineteen have died; probably as many more will die before the 1st May, and twice that number may be past the power of recovery, previous to the appearance of vegetation.

The health of the Regiment declines. Nearly all are suffering with the disease in a slight degree, or in its worst form. None improve—many grow worse. One officer, only, suffers from its influence.

It is obvious that a suitable local situation and a proper regemin, is essentially necessary to the preservation or improvement of health. How far these are within the control of the Commanding Officer they who are better acquainted with his resources, can better determine.

I would however, respectfully suggest, to the considerations of the gentlemen of the board, the propriety of providing a general Hospital establishment in some elligible situation in the vicinity of the settlements where the sick and languishing may receive suitable subsistence. The deplorable situation of our sick, demand our utmost exertion and would, in my opinion, justify any measure which may be promptly adopted for their relief.

35. *John Gale to Willoughby Morgan*[47]

CANTONMENT MISSOURI
March 19, 1820

[68–69] In conformity with your wishes, I have the honor to answer the questions you have proposed.

1st What is the number of sick under the influence of Scurvy in the Rifle Regiment.

Of the Riflemen one hundred and thirty five cases of the disease are distinctly marked; doubtless many others are tainted with it, who suffer in a less degree.

2nd. What number of Scurvy patients are confined to their beds (excluding those beyond hope of recovery) and require assistance in moving from place to place, and what number are able to set and walk about?

Of those under the influence of scurvy seventy five are confined to their beds, what number would die under favourable circumstances, is impossible to determine. The disease has, however, progressed so far that death is the inevitable fate of many. Sixty are able to sit up and with difficulty walk about.

3d What in your opinion would be the effect of retaining those of the sick at this place who would have a prospect of recovering under a proper regimen taking into consideration our present supplies?

From the rapid advancement without any appearance of convalescance in any instance, and the tale of fatal termination of the

47 Expedition Journal, 68–69.

disease it is reasonable to conclude that but few will recover if confined to their present diet.

4th What in your opinion would be the effect of removing the class of scurvy patients as low down as Fort Osage provided they could be supplied at that place with fresh Animal Food, vegetables, Milk &c?

As change of scene, air and exercise have a tendency to remove this complaint a Favorable result may be expected from removing the sick to Fort Osage, Specially if they can be supplied with the usual remedies, which consist chiefly in a diet of fresh Animal food, and recent vegetables. Milk which partakes of the nature of both Animal and vegetable food, has also great agency in restoring a Constitution decayed From erronious Diet.

5th What number of sick will it be necessary to remove if this measure should be decided on, and how many Boats will it require for the purpose?

In this event One Hundred Riflemen may I believe with propriety be removed. It will require two Boats to remove them.

6th How many attendants will the sick require?

Eight men calculated to perform this duty will be sufficient.

36. John Gale to Willoughby Morgan[48]

CANTONMENT MISSOURI
March 20, 1820

[69–71] The prevalent disease has become so alarmingly Fatal, that I would respectfully suggest the propriety of adopting some Further measures for the comfort, convenience and recovery of the Sick. Nothing I am sensible, in the power of the Commanding Officer has heretofore been left undone which could in the least alliviate our distressing situation. The breaking of the Ice now presents an other *alternative* which if embraced promises a happy result—that of establishing a Hospital and sending those who have any prospect [of] recovering under a proper regimen,

48 Expedition Journal, 69–71.

to Fort Osage. Nothing but motives of humanity and the ultimate interest of the service could enduce me to propose a measure
which may so materially effect the expedition.

When we reflect however more than one hundred have already
died, that Three Hundred and forty-five remain on the sick report, and that with all our exertions which have been extended
to the utmost of our ability no one has recovered on or in the
least degree convalesced can the propriety of the measure if it
affords any prospect of relief be doubted. Change of scene, air
and exercise have a tendency to remove the complaint. A dry
sandy elevated situation is also desirable. Our Hospital Stores
are exhausted in consequence of the liberal despensation of them
in the incipient stage of the disease. The sick are much debilitated
and are compelled to subsist on Bread and salted meat of an in-
ferior quality, when the most generous and nutritive diet is
requisite. Although all we wish cannot be procured at Fort Osage
much can be. Fresh animal food may be procured From the neighboring settlements. Hospital supplies and Groceries may be received from St Louis one Month sooner, and recent vegetable
matter will make its appearance much earlier than at this place.

. . . Fish may be caught in abundance, wild onions have there
probably already appeared, salads &c may be soon raised in the
gardens which are in a state of cultivation.

There is at present no appearance of Vegetation here although
wild vegetables will probably put a period to the Further extension of the disease. But is it reasonable to suppose that those
already under its influence, weak and debilitated by long continued sickness can be restored by vegetable matter alone in
concurrence only with a diet of salted meat divested of its nu-
tritious qualities?

As none have recovered or convalesed melancholly and dis-
pondency naturally prevails among the sick. A removal will have
a tendency to excite hope and procure cheerfulness, which will
also have an agency in the restoration of health.

Minute descrimination should be used in selecting those to

descend the River. Only those who have a prospect for a recovery, as it would be unnecessarily burthensome to send those cases are desperate, the Feelings of the latter can be assuaged by telling them they shall follow when circumstances permit.

Although all may not, many may be saved by the adoption of this measure.

37. Henry Atkinson to Thomas Jesup[49]

St. Louis, Missouri
April 6, 1820

I have sent off two keels with fresh flour, beans, corn meal, vinigar & new pork . . . . The health of the troops . . . demanded the earliest attention. I am greatly astonished that the troops at the Bluffs should have been affected with the scurvy, supplied as they were with a plenty of fresh beef & two quarts of corn a week pr man, besides, good bread & salted meat. The men have nevertheless suffered severely both there & at St Peters with the disease.

38. Adjutant General to Henry Atkinson[50]

Washington, D. C.
April 7, 1820

Congress having refused the appropriation for a further advance on the Missouri than the Council Bluffs [one] will not be made this season & the Secretary of War directs that you take measures to occupy the Post of Fort Osage with the company of Riflemen now on their march from Newport Ky & the other detachment of the 6th at Pittsfield [Massachusetts] . . . .

The Secretary of War will himself write you as soon as he can find leisure.

49 Quartermaster General, Consolidated File, Atkinson's Expedition, 1820, RG 92.
50 Adjutant General, Letters Sent, Vol. 5, RG 94.

Bibliography

I. *Primary Material—Unpublished*

American Fur Company Papers, The Missouri Historical Society, St. Louis.

Army Papers, The Missouri Historical Society, St. Louis.

Jacob Brown Letterbooks, Library of Congress, Washington.

Jacob Brown Papers, Clements Library, University of Michigan, Ann Arbor.

Choteau Collection, The Missouri Historical Society, St. Louis.

Fur Trade Papers, The Missouri Historical Society, St. Louis.

Indian Papers, The Missouri Historical Society, St. Louis.

Andrew Jackson Papers (microfilm), State Historical Society of Wisconsin, Madison.

Thomas S. Jesup Papers, Library of Congress, Washington.

Journal of the Advance Corps of the Military Branch of the Yellowstone Expedition, Coe Collection, Yale University, New Haven.

Stephen W. Kearny Papers, The Missouri Historical Society, St. Louis.

Kennerly Papers, The Missouri Historical Society, St. Louis.

Letters of Officers of the War of 1812, Dreer Collection, Historical Society of Pennsylvania, Philadelphia.

John O'Fallon Papers, The Missouri Historical Society, St. Louis.

Titian R. Peale Journal, Library of Congress, Washington.

Records of the Office of the Adjutant General, Record Group 94, National Archives, Washington.

    Early Regimental Records, 1818–20.

    Letters Received, 1818–20.

    Letters Sent, 1818–20.

Muster Rolls, 1818–20.
Orders and Circulars, 1818–20.
Post Revolutionary Commands, 1818–20.
Post Revolutionary Papers, 1818–20.
Returns of Military Posts, 1820.
Records of the Office of the Quartermaster General, Record Group 92, National Archives, Washington.
Consolidated Correspondence File, 1818–20.
Letters Received, 1818–20.
Letters Sent, 1818–20.
Records of the Office of the Secretary of War, Record Group 107, National Archives, Washington.
Letters Received, Registered Series, 1818–20.
Letters Received, Unregistered Series, 1818–20.
Letters Sent, Military Affairs, 1818–20.
Records of United States Army Commands, Record Group 98, National Archives, Washington.
Ninth Military Department, Orders and Letters, 1819–26.
Sixth Infantry, Orders and Letters, 1817–26.
William Russell Papers, The Missouri Historical Society, St. Louis.
Thomas A. Smith Papers, State Historical Society of Missouri, Columbia.
United States Army, Quartermaster Department Papers, Library of Congress, Washington.
David Todd Papers, The Missouri Historical Society, St. Louis.

II. *Primary Material—Published*

A. Articles

Hubbell, William D. "The First Steamboats on the Missouri: Reminiscences of Captain W. D. Hubbell," Vivian K. McLarty, ed., *Missouri Historical Review*, Vol. LI (July, 1957), 373–81.

Johnson, James. "The Life and Letters of James Johnson of Kentucky," James A. Padgett, ed., *Register of Kentucky State Historical Society*, Vol. XXXV (October, 1937), 301–38.

Kearny, Stephen W. "Journal of Stephen Watts Kearny," Valentine M. Porter, ed., *Missouri Historical Society Collections*, Vol. III (January, April, 1908), 8–29, 99–131.

Pratte, Bernard, Jr. "Reminiscences of Gen. Bernard Pratte, Jr.," *Missouri Historical Society Bulletin*, Vol. IV (October, 1949), 59–71.

B. Books

Audubon, John J. *Audubon's America: The Narratives and Experiences of John J. Audubon.* Ed. by Donald C. Peattie. Boston, 1940.

Bates, Frederick. *The Life and Papers of Frederick Bates.* Ed. by Thomas M. Marshall. 2 vols. St. Louis, 1926.

Bell, John R. *Journal of Captain John R. Bell, Official Journalist for the Stephen H. Long Expedition to the Rocky Mountains, 1820.* Vol. VI of the *Far West and Rockies Series*, ed. by Harlan M. Fuller and LeRoy R. Hafen. Glendale, California, 1957.

Billon, Frederic L. *Annals of St. Louis in Its Territorial Days From 1804 to 1821.* St. Louis, 1888.

Brackenridge, Henry M. *Journal of a Voyage up the River Missouri Performed in 1811.* Vol. VI of *Early Western Travels*, ed. by Reuben G. Thwaites. Cleveland, 1905.

Calhoun, John C. *Correspondence of John C. Calhoun.* American Historical Association, *Annual Report*, 1899, ed. by J. F. Jameson. Washington, 1900.

———. *The Papers of John C. Calhoun.* Ed. by Robert L. Meriwether and W. Edwin Hemphill. 2 vols. Columbia, South Carolina, 1959–63.

Clark, William. *The Field Notes of Captain William Clark, 1803–1805.* Ed. by Ernest S. Osgood. New Haven, 1964.

———. *Westward with Dragoons: The Journal of William Clark On His Expedition to Establish Fort Osage . . . 1808.* Ed. by Kate L. Gregg. Fulton, Missouri, 1937.

Gass, Patrick. *A Journal of the Voyages and Travels of a Corps of Discovery Under the Command of Capt. Lewis and Capt. Clarke . . . .* (Reprint). Minneapolis, 1958.

Houck, Louis, ed. *The Spanish Regime in Missouri.* 2 vols. Chicago, 1909.

James, Edwin. *Account of an Expedition from Pittsburgh to the Rocky Mountains Performed in the Years 1819 and '20 . . . .* Vols. XIV–XVII of *Early Western Travels*, ed. by Reuben G. Thwaites. Cleveland, 1905.

Kennerly, William C. *Persimmon Hill: A Narrative of Old St. Louis and the Far West*. As told to Elizabeth Russell. Norman, 1948.

Lewis, Meriwether, and William Clark. *History of the Expedition Under the Command of Lewis and Clark . . . Performed during the Years 1804–5–6 . . . .* Ed. by Elliott Coues. 4 vols. New York, 1893.

———. *Original Journals of the Lewis and Clark Expedition, 1804–1806, Printed from the Original Manuscripts . . . now for the first time Published in Full and Exactly as Written*. Ed. by Reuben G. Thwaites. 8 vols. New York, 1904–1905.

Peck, John M. *Forty Years of Pioneer Life: Memoir of John M. Peck, D. D. . . . .* Ed. by Rufus Babcock. Philadelphia, 1864.

Pike, Zebulon M. *The Journals of Zebulon Montgomery Pike, With Letters and Related Documents*. Ed. by Donald Jackson. 2 vols. Norman, 1966.

Poesch, Jessie. *Titian Ramsay Peale, 1799–1885, and His Journals of the Wilkes Expedition*. American Philosophical Society Memoirs, Vol. LII. Philadelphia, 1961.

Thorpe, Joseph. *Early Days in the West*. Liberty, Missouri, 1924.

C. Newspapers

Missouri Gazette and Public Advertizer (St. Louis).
Missouri Intelligencer (Franklin).
Missouri Republican (St. Louis).
National Intelligencer (Washington).
Niles Register (Baltimore).
St. Louis Beacon (Missouri).
St. Louis Enquirer (Missouri).

D. U.S. Government Publications

American State Papers: Indian Affairs. 2 vols. Washington, 1832–34.

American State Papers: Military Affairs. 7 vols. Washington, 1832–61.

Carter, Clarence E., ed. *The Territorial Papers of the United States*. 26 vols. Washington, 1934–62.

Heitman, Francis B., comp. *Historical Register and Dictionary of the United States Army, from Its Organization, September 29, 1789, to March 2, 1903*. 2 vols. Washington, 1903.

Hodge, Frederick W., ed. *Handbook of American Indians North of*

Mexico. (Bureau of American Ethnology *Bulletin 30.*) 2 vols. Washington, 1907–10.

Kappler, Charles J., comp. *Indian Affairs: Laws and Treaties.* 2 vols. Washington, 1903–1904.

Lawson, Thomas. *Statistical Report on the Sickness and Mortality of the Army of the United States.* Washington, 1840.

Miller, Hunter, ed. *Treaties and Other International Acts of the United States of America.* 8 vols. Washington, 1931–48.

The Public Statutes at Large of the United States of America, 1789–1845. 5 vols. Boston, 1848.

Risch, Erna. *Quartermaster Support of the Army: A History of the Corps 1775–1935.* Washington, 1962.

Thian, Raphael P. *Some Notes Illustrating the Military Geography of the United States, 1813–1880.* Washington, 1881.

United States Congress, "Documents in Relation to the Claim of James Johnson . . . ," March 1, 1821. 16 Cong., 2 sess., *House Executive Document No. 110.*

United States Congress, "Message of the President [James Monroe] . . . To the Senate . . . ," November 17, 1818. 15 Cong., 2 sess., *Senate Document No. 1.*

United States Department of War. *Official Army Register, 1818–20.* Washington, 1818–20.

United States Geological Service. Topographic sheets for portions of Illinois, Iowa, Kansas, Missouri, and Nebraska. Washington, 1915–63.

United States Missouri River Commission. Missouri River maps. Washington, 1892–96.

III. *Secondary Material*

A. Articles and Other Printed Material

Bagley, Gerald C. "Daniel T. Potts," in Vol. III of *The Mountain Men and the Fur Trade of the Far West,* 249–62. Ed. by LeRoy R. Hafen. Glendale, California, 1965–.

Drumm, Stella M., comp. "The Kennerlys of Virginia," *Missouri Historical Society Collections,* Vol. VI (1928), 98–123.

McDermott, John D. "John Baptiste Richard," in Vol. II of *The*

Mountain Men and the Fur Trade of the Far West, 289–303. Ed. by LeRoy R. Hafen. Glendale, California, 1965–.

McDermott, John F. "Samuel Seymour: Pioneer Artist of the Plains and Rockies," *Annual Report of the Smithsonian Institution, 1950*, 497–509. Washington, 1951.

Wesley, Edgar B. "A Still Larger View of the So-Called Yellowstone Expedition," *North Dakota Historical Quarterly*, Vol. V (July, 1931), 219–38.

B. Books

Ashburn, Percy M. *A History of the Medical Department of the United States Army*. Boston, 1929.

Beers, Henry P. *The Western Military Frontier, 1815–1846*. Philadelphia, 1935.

Bell, Ovid. *Cote Sans Dessein: A History*. Fulton, Missouri, 1930.

The Biographical Encyclopedia of Kentucky, of the Dead and Living Men of the Nineteenth Century. Cincinnati, 1878.

Chittenden, Hiram M. *The American Fur Trade of the Far West*. 3 vols. New York, 1902.

Clarke, Dwight L. *Stephen Watts Kearny: Soldier of the West*. Norman, 1961.

Coles, Harry L. *The War of 1812*. Chicago, 1965.

Conrad, Howard L., ed. *Encyclopedia of the History of Missouri*. 8 vols. St. Louis, 1901.

Funk and Wagnall's New "Standard" Dictionary of the English Language . . . . 1953 ed. New York, 1953.

Gale, George. *The Gale Family Records in England and the United States*. Galesville, Wisconsin, 1866.

Goetzman, William H. *Army Exploration in the American West 1803–1865*. New Haven, 1959.

Hagan, William T. *The Sac and Fox Indians*. Norman, 1958.

Hickman, W. Z. *History of Jackson County, Missouri*. Cleveland, 1920.

History of Carroll County, Missouri . . . . St. Louis, 1881.

History of Clay and Platte Counties, Missouri . . . . St. Louis, 1885.

History of Howard and Chariton Counties, Missouri . . . . St. Louis, 1883.

History of Howard and Cooper Counties, Missouri . . . . St. Louis, 1883.

History of Lafayette County, Missouri . . . . St. Louis, 1881.

History of Ray County, Missouri . . . . St. Louis, 1881.

History of St. Charles, Montgomery, and Warren Counties, Missouri . . . . St. Louis, 1885.

History of Saline County, Missouri . . . . St. Louis, 1881.

Houck, Louis. *A History of Missouri From the Earliest Explorations and Settlements Until the Admission of the State into the Union.* 3 vols. Chicago, 1908.

Johnson, Allen, and Dumas Malone, eds. *Dictionary of American Biography.* 20 vols. New York, 1928–36.

Johnson, William F. *History of Cooper County, Missouri.* Cleveland, 1919.

Morgan, Dale. *Jedediah Smith and the Opening of the West.* Indianapolis, 1953.

Nichols, Roger L. *General Henry Atkinson: A Western Military Career.* Norman, 1965.

Oglesby, Richard E. *Manuel Lisa and the Opening of the Missouri Fur Trade.* Norman, 1963.

Peake, Ora B. *A History of the United States Indian Factory System.* Denver, 1954.

Potter, Chandler E. *The Military History of the State of New Hampshire.* Concord, N. H., 1866.

Prucha, Francis P. *American Indian Policy in the Formative Years: The Indian Trade and Intercourse Acts, 1780–1834.* Cambridge, Massachusetts, 1962.

———. *Guide to the Military Posts of the United States.* Madison, 1964.

Ramsay, Robert L. *The Place Names of Franklin County, Missouri.* Vol. XXVI of the University of Missouri *Studies,* No. 3. Columbia, Missouri, 1954.

Redford, Albert H. *Life and Times of Hubbard H. Kavanaugh, D. D.* Nashville, 1884.

Smith, T. Berry, and Pearl S. Gehrig. *History of Chariton and Howard Counties, Missouri.* Indianapolis, 1923.

Stephen, Leslie, and Sidney Lee, eds. *Dictionary of National Biography.* 63 vols. New York, 1885–1900.

Webster's Third New International Dictionary of the English Language . . . . Chicago and Cambridge, Massachusetts, 1961.

Wesley, Edgar B. *Guarding the Frontier: A Study of Frontier Defense from 1815–1825.* Minneapolis, 1935.

Wheat, Carl I. *Mapping the Transmississippi West, 1540–1861.* 5 vols. San Francisco, 1957–63.

Withington, Mary C., comp. *A Catalogue of Manuscripts in the Collection of Western Americana Founded by William Robertson Coe.* New Haven, 1952.

Wood, Richard G. *Stephen Harriman Long, 1784–1864: Army Engineer, Explorer, Inventor.* Glendale, California, 1966.

Index

135

of which *The Missouri Expedition, 1818–1820: The Journal of Surgeon John Gale* is Number 56, was started in 1939 by the University of Oklahoma Press. It follows rather logically the Press's program of regional exploration. Behind the story of the gradual and inevitable recession of the American frontier lie the accounts of explorers, traders, and travelers, which individually and in the aggregate present one of the most romantic and fascinating chapters in the development of the American domain. The following list is complete as of the date of publication of this volume.

1. Captain Randolph B. Marcy and Captain George B. McClellan. *Adventure on Red River*: Report on the Exploration of the Headwaters of the Red River. Edited by Grant Foreman.
2. Grant Foreman. *Marcy and the Gold Seekers*: The Journal of Captain R. B. Marcy, with an account of the Gold Rush over the Southern Route.
3. Pierre-Antoine Tabeau. *Tabeau's Narrative of Loisel's Expedition to the Upper Missouri*. Edited by Annie Heloise Abel. Translated from the French by Rose Abel Wright.
4. Victor Tixier. *Tixier's Travels on the Osage Prairies*. Edited by John Francis McDermott. Translated from the French by Albert J. Salvan.
5. Teodoro de Croix. *Teodoro de Croix and the Northern Frontier of New Spain, 1776–1783*. Translated from the Spanish and edited by Alfred Barnaby Thomas.
6. A. W. Whipple. *A Pathfinder in the Southwest*: The Itinerary of Lieutenant A. W. Whipple During His Exploration for a Railway Route from Fort Smith to Los Angeles in the Years 1853 & 1854. Edited and annotated by Grant Foreman.
7. Josiah Gregg. *Diary & Letters of Josiah Gregg*. Edited by Maurice Garland Fulton. Introductions by Paul Horgan. Two volumes.
8. Washington Irving. *The Western Journals of Washington Irving*. Edited and annotated by John Francis McDermott.
9. Edward Dumbauld. *Thomas Jefferson, American Tourist*: Being an Account of His Journeys in the United States of America, England, France, Italy, the Low Countries, and Germany. Out of print.

10. Victor Wolfgang von Hagen. *Maya Explorer*: John Lloyd Stephens and the Lost Cities of Central America and Yucatán.
11. E. Merton Coulter. *Travels in the Confederate States*: A Bibliography.
12. W. Eugene Hollon. *The Lost Pathfinder*: Zebulon Montgomery Pike. Out of print.
13. George Frederick Ruxton. *Ruxton of the Rockies*. Collected by Clyde and Mae Reed Porter. Edited by LeRoy R. Hafen. Out of print.
14. George Frederick Ruxton. *Life in the Far West*. Edited by LeRoy R. Hafen. Foreword by Mae Reed Porter.
15. Edward Harris. *Up the Missouri with Audubon*: The Journal of Edward Harris. Edited by John Francis McDermott.
16. Robert Stuart. *On the Oregon Trail*: Robert Stuart's Journey of Discovery (1812–1831). Edited by Kenneth A. Spaulding.
17. Josiah Gregg. *Commerce of the Prairies*. Edited by Max L. Moorhead.
18. John Treat Irving, Jr. *Indian Sketches*: Taken During an Expedition to the Pawnee Tribes (1833). Edited and annotated by John Francis McDermott.
19. Thomas D. Clark (ed.). *Travels in the Old South, 1527–1860*: A Bibliography. Three volumes. Volumes One and Two issued as a set (1956); Volume Three (1959). Out of print.
20. Alexander Ross. *The Fur Hunters of the Far West*. Edited by Kenneth A. Spaulding.
21. William Bollaert. *William Bollaert's Texas*. Edited by W. Eugene Hollon and Ruth Lapham Butler. Out of print.
22. Daniel Ellis Conner. *Joseph Reddeford Walker and the Arizona Adventure*. Edited by Donald J. Berthrong and Odessa Davenport.
23. Matthew C. Field. *Prairie and Mountain Sketches*. Collected by Clyde and Mae Reed Porter. Edited by Kate L. Gregg and John Francis McDermott.
24. Ross Cox. *The Columbia River*: Scenes and Adventures During a Residence of Six Years on the Western Side of the Rocky Mountains Among Various Tribes of Indians Hitherto Unknown; Together with a Journey Across the American Continent. Edited by Edgar I. and Jane R. Stewart.
25. Noel M. Loomis. *The Texan–Santa Fé Pioneers*.

26. Charles Preuss. *Exploring with Frémont*: The Private Diaries of Charles Preuss, Cartographer for John C. Frémont on His First, Second, and Fourth Expeditions to the Far West. Translated and edited by Erwin G. and Elisabeth K. Gudde.
27. Jacob H. Schiel. *Journey Through the Rocky Mountains and the Humboldt Mountains to the Pacific Ocean.* Translated from the German and edited by Thomas N. Bonner.
28. Zenas Leonard. *Adventures of Zenas Leonard, Fur Trader.* Edited by John C. Ewers.
29. Matthew C. Field. *Matt Field on the Santa Fe Trail.* Collected by Clyde and Mae Reed Porter. Edited and with an introduction and notes by John E. Sunder.
30. James Knox Polk Miller. *The Road to Virginia City*: The Diary of James Knox Polk Miller. Edited by Andrew F. Rolle.
31. Benjamin Butler Harris. *The Gila Trail*: The Texas Argonauts and the California Gold Rush. Edited and annotated by Richard H. Dillon.
32. Lieutenant James H. Bradley. *The March of the Montana Column*: A Prelude to the Custer Disaster. Edited by Edgar I. Stewart.
33. Heinrich Lienhard. *From St. Louis to Sutter's Fort, 1846.* Translated and edited by Erwin G. and Elisabeth K. Gudde.
34. Washington Irving. *The Adventures of Captain Bonneville.* Edited and with an introduction by Edgeley W. Todd.
35. Jean-Bernard Bossu. *Jean-Bernard Bossu's Travels in the Interior of North America, 1751–1762.* Translated and edited by Seymour Feiler.
36. Thomas D. Clark (ed.). *Travels in the New South, 1865–1955*: A Bibliography. Two volumes.
37. John Lloyd Stephens. *Incidents of Travels in Yucatán.* Edited and with an introduction by Victor Wolfgang von Hagen. Two volumes.
38. Richard A. Bartlett. *Great Surveys of the American West.*
39. Gloria Griffen Cline. *Exploring the Great Basin.*
40. Francisco de Miranda. *The New Democracy in America*: The Travels of Francisco de Miranda in the United States, 1783–84. Translated by Judson P. Wood. Edited by John S. Ezell.
41. Colonel Joseph K. F. Mansfield. *Mansfield on the Condition of the Western Forts, 1853–54.* Edited by Robert W. Frazer.

by Seymour Feiler. Edited, with an introduction and notes, by George F. Spaulding.
55. Robert R. Miller. *For Science and National Glory*: The Spanish Scientific Expedition to America, 1862–1866.
56. John Gale. *The Missouri Expedition 1818–1820*: The Journal of Surgeon John Gale. Edited, with an introduction and notes, by Roger L. Nichols.

THE MISSOURI EXPEDITION 1818–1820 was machine type-set in eleven-point Linotype Baskerville, a revival of the cele-brated typeface created by John Baskerville, eighteenth-century English type founder.

The display type is handset Garamond Italic, another face in use at the time of the Missouri Expedition. Because of its narrow letter forms and extreme italic slant, Garamond Italic suggests the handwriting in the Gale Journal. Italics were used liberally in the text for the same reason.

The paper on which this book is printed bears the watermark of the University of Oklahoma Press and is designed to have an effective life of over three hundred years.

UNIVERSITY OF OKLAHOMA PRESS

NORMAN